# Student Activity Guide for
# Working with Young Children

by

**Dr. Judy Herr**
Professor, Early Childhood Development
College of Human Development
University of Wisconsin-Stout
Menomonie, Wisconsin

Publisher
**The Goodheart-Willcox Company, Inc.**
Tinley Park, Illinois

# Introduction

This activity guide is designed for use with the text *Working with Young Children*. It will help you recall, review, and expand on the concepts presented in the text. It will also help you understand how to meet children's developmental needs as you teach and care for them.

The best way to use this activity guide is to begin by reading your assignment in the text. You will find that the activities in the activity guide correspond to the chapters in the text. Follow the instructions carefully at the beginning of each activity.

You will find a variety of activities in this guide. Some activities, such as true/false and matching activities, review text information. These can be used as study guides as you review in preparation for quizzes and tests. Do your best to complete these activities carefully and accurately. Try to complete as much of each activity as you can without referring to the text. Then compare the answers you have to the information in *Working with Young Children*. At that time you can also complete any questions you could not answer.

Other activities will ask for your ideas, opinions, evaluations, and conclusions that cannot be judged as right or wrong. The object of these activities is to encourage you to consider alternatives and evaluate situations thoughtfully. The text will be a useful reference in completing these activities.

The activities in this guide have been designed to be both interesting and fun to do. This activity guide will help you apply what you have learned as you work with children now and in the future.

# Contents

# Part Two
# Creating a Safe and Healthy Environment

# Part Three
# Guiding Children

## Part Four
## Learning Experiences for Children

## Part Five
## Other People You Will Meet

# You: Working with Young Children

## Truths About Early Childhood

**Activity A**

**Chapter 1**

Name _____

Date _____ Period_____

Read the following statements. Circle *T* if the statement is true or *F* if the statement is false.

T  F  1.  Early childhood covers the period from birth to nine years of age.

T  F  2.  Social and economic changes will continue to create a need for more early childhood services.

T  F  3.  Fewer than half of all preschool children are in early childhood programs.

T  F  4.  The number of single parent families has decreased since 1960.

T  F  5.  Corporate-sponsored child care will continue to grow in the future.

T  F  6.  Companies have found that providing child care has a negative effect on morale and absenteeism.

T  F  7.  There are more opportunities in early childhood now than ever before.

T  F  8.  Full-day kindergartens are increasing in number.

T  F  9.  In the future, there will most likely be a greater allocation of public dollars for early childhood education.

T  F  10.  Nannies work in their own homes to care for children.

T  F  11.  An au pair is a person from a foreign country who provides child care.

T  F  12.  Kindergarten teachers only work in public schools.

T  F  13.  A child care director recruits children, hires and supervises staff, and manages the budget.

T  F  14.  The teacher in a child care center has broader responsibilities than the director.

T  F  15.  Licensing specialists are employed by the state to ensure that state rules and regulations are followed.

T  F  16.  Parent educators may design written materials to help parents better understand their roles and the nature of young children.

T  F  17.  To be a teacher's aide, a person needs an associate degree.

T  F  18.  To obtain the CDA Credential, you must take courses in early childhood education.

# Comparing Teaching to Other Careers

Name _____

Date _____ Period_____

Before making a career choice, you should compare several careers. In the chart below, use descriptive phrases to show how teaching compares in each area with another career that interests you.

| CATEGORY | TEACHING | CAREER: _____ |
|---|---|---|
| Preparation and education required | | |
| Primary job responsibilities | | |
| Workplace environment | | |
| Pay | | |
| Relationships with coworkers | | |
| Communication skills needed | | |
| Time management skills needed | | |
| Continuing education suggested | | |
| Satisfaction gained from career | | |

# Pleasures and Problems in Teaching

Activity C

Name _____

Chapter 1

Date _____ Period _____

Listed below are typical activities of early childhood teachers. Read the activities and indicate whether you feel each activity would be pleasant, unpleasant, or if you are unsure.

| Pleasant | Unpleasant | Unsure | | |
|----------|------------|--------|---|---|
| _____ | _____ | _____ | 1. | Rocking children to sleep. |
| _____ | _____ | _____ | 2. | Meeting new parents. |
| _____ | _____ | _____ | 3. | Changing diapers. |
| _____ | _____ | _____ | 4. | Teaching children to dress themselves. |
| _____ | _____ | _____ | 5. | Writing parent letters. |
| _____ | _____ | _____ | 6. | Selecting new equipment. |
| _____ | _____ | _____ | 7. | Reading stories. |
| _____ | _____ | _____ | 8. | Helping children cope with fears. |
| _____ | _____ | _____ | 9. | Comforting sad children. |
| _____ | _____ | _____ | 10. | Teaching songs to children. |
| _____ | _____ | _____ | 11. | Designing bulletin boards. |
| _____ | _____ | _____ | 12. | Arranging the classroom. |
| _____ | _____ | _____ | 13. | Selecting art activities. |
| _____ | _____ | _____ | 14. | Attending conferences. |
| _____ | _____ | _____ | 15. | Reading articles on child growth and development. |
| _____ | _____ | _____ | 16. | Settling disputes between children. |
| _____ | _____ | _____ | 17. | Taking field trips. |
| _____ | _____ | _____ | 18. | Telling puppet stories. |
| _____ | _____ | _____ | 19. | Wiping up spills. |
| _____ | _____ | _____ | 20. | Coping with temper tantrums. |
| _____ | _____ | _____ | 21. | Planning holiday parties. |
| _____ | _____ | _____ | 22. | Teaching safety. |
| _____ | _____ | _____ | 23. | Planning nutritious meals and snacks. |
| _____ | _____ | _____ | 24. | Laughing with children. |
| _____ | _____ | _____ | 25. | Recording children's progress. |

List the activities that you would consider most pleasant and explain why.

_____

_____

_____

_____

_____

*(Continued)*

List the activities that you would consider most unpleasant.

_____

_____

_____

_____

_____

_____

_____

Review your responses. Do you feel certain or uncertain about becoming an early childhood teacher? For what reasons do you feel this way?

_____

_____

_____

_____

_____

_____

# Characteristics for Working with Children

**Activity D**

**Chapter 1**

Name _____

Date _____ Period_____

People who enjoy working with young children tend to have certain characteristics in common. Many of these characteristics are listed below. For each of the characteristics, rate yourself as **(S)** strong, **(A)** average, or **(W)** weak. Then have a family member or friend rate you on the same set of characteristics using the form on the following page.

_____ Active

_____ Affectionate

_____ Alert

_____ Ambitious

_____ Artistic

_____ Broad-minded

_____ Calm

_____ Capable

_____ Careful

_____ Competent

_____ Considerate

_____ Cooperative

_____ Creative

_____ Dependable

_____ Eager

_____ Efficient

_____ Energetic

_____ Enthusiastic

_____ Firm

_____ Flexible

_____ Friendly

_____ Healthy

_____ Honest

_____ Humorous

_____ Intelligent

_____ Kind

_____ Levelheaded

_____ Likable

_____ Nurturing

_____ Organized

_____ Patient

_____ Practical

_____ Realistic

_____ Resourceful

_____ Responsible

_____ Self-controlled

_____ Sensible

_____ Serious

_____ Sincere

_____ Stable

_____ Thorough

_____ Tolerant

_____ Understanding

_____ Warm

_____ Well-groomed

_____ Wholesome

Write in additional characteristics that you feel should describe someone who works with young children. Also rate yourself in those areas.

_____ _____

_____ _____

_____ _____

_____ _____

_____ _____

*(Continued)*

In the space below, have a family member or friend rate you as **(S)** strong, **(A)** average, or **(W)** weak for each characteristic.

| | | | |
|---|---|---|---|
| _____ Active | _____ Humorous |
| _____ Affectionate | _____ Intelligent |
| _____ Alert | _____ Kind |
| _____ Ambitious | _____ Levelheaded |
| _____ Artistic | _____ Likable |
| _____ Broad-minded | _____ Nurturing |
| _____ Calm | _____ Organized |
| _____ Capable | _____ Patient |
| _____ Careful | _____ Practical |
| _____ Competent | _____ Realistic |
| _____ Considerate | _____ Resourceful |
| _____ Cooperative | _____ Responsible |
| _____ Creative | _____ Self-controlled |
| _____ Dependable | _____ Sensible |
| _____ Eager | _____ Serious |
| _____ Efficient | _____ Sincere |
| _____ Energetic | _____ Stable |
| _____ Enthusiastic | _____ Thorough |
| _____ Firm | _____ Tolerant |
| _____ Flexible | _____ Understanding |
| _____ Friendly | _____ Warm |
| _____ Healthy | _____ Well-groomed |
| _____ Honest | _____ Wholesome |

How would the characteristics in which you are strong benefit you in a career working with young children?

_____

_____

_____

_____

_____

What actions can you take to strengthen the areas in which you are weak?

_____

_____

_____

_____

# Types of Early Childhood Programs

## Early Childhood Fill-In

**Activity A**

**Chapter 2**

Name _____

Date _____ Period_____

Based on information in the text, complete each of the following sentences by writing the correct word or words in the blanks on the left.

_____ 1. Most parents who enroll children in a full-day program are highly influenced by the _____ of the program.

_____ 2. With_____, children go to their homes after school and receive calls from workers to verify they have arrived safely.

_____ 3. _____ in Montessori schools involve learning to button, zip, tie, and put on coats and boots.

_____ 4. Some companies provide a _____ service that matches the parents' needs with specific centers.

_____ 5. The primary goal of the _____ is for children to "learn how to learn."

_____ 6. Child care centers sponsored by _____ help reduce the conflict between home and work.

_____ 7. _____ is an example of a publicly sponsored program.

_____ 8. A large percentage of parents choose child care programs based on the advice of _____.

_____ 9. The emphasis of _____ care is on keeping the environment safe and healthy for young children.

_____ 10. _____ child care programs are funded by governments, school districts, or social service agencies.

_____ 11. Some kindergartens focus more on _____ development than on preacademic skills.

_____ 12. The largest group of privately sponsored programs is the _____.

_____ 13. The most common type of child care in the United States provided other than by a relative or parent is _____.

_____ 14. Fees charged at a _____ are often less than at other programs.

_____ 15. _____ is stressed in Montessori schools.

# Types of Programs

Activity B

Chapter 2

Name _____

Date _____ Period_____

Listed below are sentences describing the types of early childhood programs. Read each sentence and write the letter of the type of program it best describes. Letters will be used more than once.

_____ 1. Dental, medical, and mental health services are provided for children.

_____ 2. Interaction between the child and materials is highly structured.

_____ 3. Licensing rules for this type of child care are difficult to enforce.

_____ 4. May focus on providing a place for custodial care while parents or guardians are at work or school.

_____ 5. Stress the theory that children learn best by being active.

_____ 6. Stress vocational education for future child care professionals.

_____ 7. Exist to provide training for future teachers and to serve as a study group for research.

_____ 8. Allow secondary students to work with the preschool children of high school students, faculty, and community members.

_____ 9. Are part of many school systems today and require children to be at least five years old.

_____ 10. Enrolled children spend about half the day in creative activities.

_____ 11. Developed to meet the developmental needs of children from low-income homes.

_____ 12. Five- to ten-year-old children most often attend.

_____ 13. The teacher may experience a lack of control due to parent involvement.

_____ 14. Most common type of child care in the United States.

_____ 15. Usually open early in the morning and stay open until early evening.

_____ 16. Formed and run by parents who wish to take part in their children's preschool experiences.

_____ 17. Provide care before or after school hours.

_____ 18. Provide nutritious meals for many children who do not receive well-balanced meals at home.

_____ 19. The teacher's role is more passive than in other programs.

_____ 20. Child care is provided in a private home.

_____ 21. Parents make the administrative decisions.

_____ 22. Are located on postsecondary or college campuses.

A. child care centers

B. family child care

C. Head Start programs

D. kindergartens

E. laboratory schools

F. school-age child care

G. Montessori schools

H. parent cooperatives

I. high school child care programs

# Choosing a Program

Name _____

Date _____ Period_____

Read each of the following situations and choose the type of early childhood program that you feel would be best. Explain why you chose each program.

1. Mary had a baby six weeks ago. She promised her employer that she would return to work. Now she needs to make child care arrangements. She prefers to have her child cared for with only two or three other children. What type of care is Mary looking for?

2. Sung Lee and Lia both work eight hours a day. Total travel time to and from work takes another hour and a half. They are seeking child care in a group setting within a few miles of their home. What kind of program would be best for Sung Lee and Lia?

*(Continued)*

3. Joyce is a single, unemployed mother. She has twin three-year-olds who are having speech problems. What type of program would meet Joyce's needs for her children?

4. Larry and Marge want their daughter, Lori, to become independent. They also want a program that stresses academic learning. What type of program would meet Larry and Marge's needs?

5. Phil and Maria have a seven-year-old daughter, Elisa. They need care for Elisa from four to six o'clock each evening. In what type of program might Elisa participate?

# Evaluating Early Childhood Programs

**Activity D**

**Chapter 2**

Name _____

Date _____ Period_____

Pretend you are a parent looking for an early childhood program for your child. Visit two centers and evaluate them by checking the appropriate answers to the questions listed below. Then summarize your overall impressions of each program. Tell which one you would choose for your child and why.

Name of center #1: _____

Name of center #2: _____

| Questions to Ask | Center #1 | | Center #2 | |
|---|---|---|---|---|
| | Yes | No | Yes | No |
| 1. Is the center accredited by the National Academy of Early Childhood Programs? | | | | |
| 2. Do the children appear to be happy, active, and secure? | | | | |
| 3. Are all staff members educationally qualified? | | | | |
| 4. Do staff members attend in-service training, professional meetings, and conferences on a regular basis? | | | | |
| 5. Are staff meetings conducted regularly to plan and evaluate program activities? | | | | |
| 6. Do staff members observe, assess, and record each child's developmental progress? | | | | |
| 7. Does the curriculum support the children's individual rates of development? | | | | |
| 8. Do the staff and the curriculum celebrate diversity? | | | | |
| 9. Is the indoor and outdoor environment large enough to support a variety of activities? | | | | |
| 10. Is the environment inviting, warm, and stimulating? | | | | |
| 11. Is equipment provided to meet all four areas of development: social, emotional, cognitive, and physical? | | | | |
| 12. Are safe and sanitary conditions maintained within the building and on the play yard? | | | | |
| 13. Are teacher-child interactions positive? | | | | |
| 14. Are teachers using developmentally appropriate teaching strategies? | | | | |
| 15. Are parents welcome to observe and participate? | | | | |
| 16. Is sufficient equipment available for the number of children attending? | | | | |
| 17. Does the climate in the center "feel" positive? | | | | |
| 18. Do teachers meet with parents regularly to discuss the child's needs, interests, and abilities? | | | | |

*(Continued)*

Name _____

Overall impressions of center #1: _____

_____

_____

_____

_____

_____

Overall impressions of center #2: _____

_____

_____

_____

_____

_____

Which center would you choose and why? _____

_____

_____

_____

_____

_____

# Observing Children: A Tool for Assessment

## Check Your Understanding

Activity A

Chapter 3

Name _____

Date _____ Period_____

Read the following statements related to assessment. Circle *T* if the statement is true or *F* if the statement is false.

T   F   1.   Observation is one of the newest methods of learning about children.

T   F   2.   Assessment is the process of observing, recording, and documenting children's growth and behavior over time.

T   F   3.   Evaluation is the process of reviewing the information and finding value in it.

T   F   4.   Assessment keeps the teacher and curriculum responsive to the needs of children.

T   F   5.   A child's strengths and weaknesses can be identified through the assessment process.

T   F   6.   A single assessment is an exact assessment of ability or performance.

T   F   7.   Formal assessment is often used by early childhood teachers.

T   F   8.   Developmental norms are characteristic behaviors considered normal for children in specific age groups.

T   F   9.   Teachers prefer to use only one method for gathering information about the children.

T   F   10.  Anecdotal records are the simplest form of direct observation.

T   F   11.  Anecdotal records should include generalizations about the motives, attitudes, and feelings of the children.

T   F   12.  Observations should always be factual and unbiased.

T   F   13.  An anecdotal record requires no special setting or time frame.

T   F   14.  An interpretation attempts to explain observed behavior and give it meaning.

T   F   15.  Interpretations may be influenced by feelings, values, and attitudes.

T   F   16.  Checklists may be developed to survey one child or a group of children.

T   F   17.  Using a participation chart, teachers sometimes find children's activity preferences do not match their needs.

T   F   18.  Rating scales require you to make a judgment about behavior.

T   F   19.  A child's random scribbles on paper are not needed for assessment purposes.

T   F   20.  A portfolio can show the child's growth and development over time.

# Assessment Tools Summary

Name _____

Date _____ Period _____

For each of the assessment tools listed, give possible advantages and disadvantages to their use. Then give an instance when this tool could effectively be used. Use your text to complete the chart as much as possible. Use other references or give your own opinion in order to complete the remaining portions of this chart.

| Anecdotal Records | | |
|---|---|---|
| Advantages: | Disadvantages: | Use: |
| | | |

| Checklists | | |
|---|---|---|
| Advantages: | Disadvantages: | Use: |
| | | |

*(Continued)*

| Participation Chart | | |
|---|---|---|
| Advantages: | Disadvantages: | Use: |
| | | |

| Rating Scale | | |
|---|---|---|
| Advantages: | Disadvantages: | Use: |
| | | |

# Interpreting the Data

**Activity C**  Name _____

**Chapter 3**  Date _____ Period_____

Read the incident recorded on the anecdotal record shown in Figure 3-6 of your text. Then try your hand at interpreting the data by answering the questions below. Compare your interpretation with a classmate's and answer the remaining questions.

**Your interpretation:**

1. Why did Carrie hit and push Tony?_____
   _____

2. What might have been her motive? _____
   _____

3. Could someone or something have caused Carrie to act this way? _____
   _____

4. Why did Carrie smile as Tony left?_____
   _____

5. Why did Tony respond as he did when he was hit and shoved?_____
   _____

6. What might have been his motive for shrugging and walking away? _____
   _____

7. Could someone or something have caused Tony to act this way? _____
   _____

**Comparing interpretations:**

Since no two people interpret facts in the same way, read the interpretation of this incident written by one of your classmates.

1. How did your classmate's interpretation differ from yours?_____
   _____
   _____
   _____

2. What explanation can you give for this difference? _____
   _____
   _____
   _____

3. What conclusions can you draw from this comparison?_____
   _____
   _____
   _____

# Designing an Assessment Tool

**Activity D**

**Chapter 3**

Name _____

Date _____ Period_____

Teachers often create their own assessment tools to meet their specific classroom needs. Design a simple checklist in the space provided below. Use the developmental milestones information in the Appendix of your text to make your checklist. Also refer to the samples in your text. Write the behaviors to be assessed in the column on the left. Then use your checklist to assess a child.

Age of child for which this checklist is designed: _____

Category of skill(s) being assessed (fine motor, gross motor, self-help skills, etc.): _____

_____

|  | Yes | No |
|---|---|---|
|  |  |  |
|  |  |  |
|  |  |  |
|  |  |  |
|  |  |  |
|  |  |  |
|  |  |  |
|  |  |  |
|  |  |  |
|  |  |  |
|  |  |  |
|  |  |  |
|  |  |  |
|  |  |  |
|  |  |  |
|  |  |  |
|  |  |  |
|  |  |  |
|  |  |  |
|  |  |  |
|  |  |  |
|  |  |  |

# Understanding Children from Birth to Age Two

**4**

## Types of Development

Activity A

Chapter 4

Name _____

Date _____ Period_____

Read each of the following skills and behaviors. Then place a check in the column that identifies the type of development being illustrated by each skill or behavior.

| | Physical Development | Cognitive Development | Social-Emotional Development |
|---|---|---|---|
| 1. Recognizes the voice of a parent. | | | |
| 2. Gives "just two" on request. | | | |
| 3. Answers routine questions. | | | |
| 4. Understands *smaller*. | | | |
| 5. Rides a tricycle. | | | |
| 6. Smiles at a familiar face. | | | |
| 7. Can point to body parts. | | | |
| 8. Understands the pronoun *we*. | | | |
| 9. Creeps. | | | |
| 10. Does not like to share toys. | | | |
| 11. Counts to five. | | | |
| 12. Points to a circle. | | | |
| 13. Understands *same size*. | | | |
| 14. Marches to music. | | | |
| 15. Says no just to see what will happen. | | | |
| 16. Tells original stories. | | | |
| 17. Hurls a ball. | | | |
| 18. Follows a three-step command. | | | |
| 19. Is patient and generous. | | | |
| 20. Jumps in place. | | | |

# Reflexes

Name _____

Date _____ Period _____

Write a brief statement describing the behavior exhibited with each of the reflexes listed below.

1. Rooting: _____

   _____

   _____

   _____

   _____

2. Moro: _____

   _____

   _____

   _____

   _____

3. Palmar grasp: _____

   _____

   _____

   _____

   _____

4. Babinski: _____

   _____

   _____

   _____

   _____

5. Stepping or walking: _____

   _____

   _____

   _____

   _____

# Understanding Development

Name _____

Date _____ Period_____

Complete the following sentences by writing the correct words in the blanks.

| | | |
|---|---|---|
| attachment | infant | reflex |
| cognitive | motor sequence | separation anxiety |
| deferred imitation | object permanence | social-emotional |
| fine motor | physical | temperament |
| gross motor | preschooler | toddler |

_____ 1. A(n) _____ is an automatic body response to a stimulus.

_____ 2. A child is called a(n) _____ during the first year after birth.

_____ 3. The understanding that objects exist even if you cannot see them is known as _____.

_____ 4. When a child is unhappy because a caregiver is leaving, the child is showing _____.

_____ 5. Children demonstrate _____ by watching another person's behavior and acting it out later.

_____ 6. _____ development involves the improvement of skills using large muscles.

_____ 7. _____ behaviors show that infants care for and respond to certain people who are important to them.

_____ 8. _____ development involves learning to relate to others and refining feelings and expressions of feelings.

_____ 9. The way a child reacts to his or her environment reflects the child's _____.

_____ 10. _____ development refers to changes in the body.

_____ 11. The term _____ refers to the order in which a child is able to perform new movements.

_____ 12. The term which describes a child who is between the ages of three and six years is _____.

_____ 13. _____ development involves skills which relate to the small muscles.

_____ 14. From the first year until the third birthday, a child is called a(n) _____.

_____ 15. _____ development refers to the mental processes used to gain knowledge.

# Encouraging Development

Name _____

Date _____ Period _____

Talk with an early childhood teacher to learn about activities, equipment, objects, and teaching approaches he or she uses to encourage development in children from birth to two years of age. Seek information related to each area of development listed. Record your findings below and share them with the class.

Physical development:

_____

_____

_____

_____

_____

_____

_____

_____

_____

Cognitive development:

_____

_____

_____

_____

_____

_____

_____

_____

_____

Social-emotional development:

_____

_____

_____

_____

_____

_____

_____

_____

_____

# Understanding Two- and Three-Year-Olds

## Development of Two-Year-Olds

**Activity A**            Name _____

**Chapter 5**             Date _____ Period_____

Use the information in the text to answer the following questions about two-year-olds.

1. What advances in the area of gross motor development are usually observed in two-year-olds? _____
   _____
   _____
   _____

2. What advances in the area of fine motor development are usually observed in two-year-olds? _____
   _____
   _____
   _____

3. Explain the difference between comprehension skills and expressive language skills. Which skills do
   children develop sooner? _____
   _____
   _____
   _____

4. What math readiness skills do two-year-olds have? _____
   _____
   _____
   _____

5. What types of experiences do two-year-olds enjoy acting out as they play? _____
   _____
   _____

6. How do most two-year-olds feel about possessions and what actions display this attitude? _____
   _____
   _____

*(Continued)*

7. Why are fears so common among two-year-olds? _____

_____

_____

8. How can a teacher encourage a two-year-old's emotional development? _____

_____

_____

9. List at least four important considerations for teachers of two-year-olds.

_____

_____

_____

# Studying Two-Year-Olds

**Activity B**                    Name _____

**Chapter 5**                     Date _____ Period_____

Interview one or both parents of a two-year-old child. Ask how that child has developed and changed in the past year in relation to each of the areas listed. If necessary, explain each type of development to the parent or parents you are interviewing. Then compare the child's actual development with the usual development for two-year-olds as described in the text.

| Gross motor development | Fine motor development |
|---|---|
| **Self-help skills** | **Language comprehension** |
| **Expressive language skills** | **Math readiness** |
| **Social development** | **Emotional development** |

What usual developments of two-year-olds has this child not yet achieved?_____

_____

_____

_____

_____

In what ways has this child matured beyond the level of most two-year-olds? _____

_____

_____

_____

# Development of Three-Year-Olds

**Activity C**     Name _____

**Chapter 5**     Date _____ Period _____

Use the text to answer the following questions about three-year-olds.

1. What new gross motor skills do three-year-olds have?_____
   _____
   _____

2. List some new fine motor skills of three-year-olds. _____
   _____
   _____
   _____
   _____

3. In what way are the thinking skills of the three-year-old more mature than the thinking skills of the two-year-old?
   _____
   _____

4. What flaws still exist in the three-year-old's ability to think? _____
   _____
   _____

5. What new language comprehension skills do three-year-olds develop?_____
   _____
   _____
   _____
   _____

6. What new expressive language skills do three-year-olds develop?_____
   _____
   _____
   _____

7. What new math readiness developments can be observed in three-year-olds?_____
   _____
   _____
   _____

8. How does a three-year-old's attitude toward possessions differ from a two-year-old's attitude toward possessions?_____
   _____
   _____
   _____

*(Continued)*

9. How do three-year-olds handle their emotions? _____

_____

_____

_____

10. How do three-year-olds usually express their anger? _____

_____

_____

11. What are four important considerations when teaching three-year-olds?_____

_____

_____

_____

_____

# Studying Three-Year-Olds

Name _____

Date _____ Period_____

Interview one or both parents of a three-year-old child. Ask how that child has developed and changed in the past year in relation to each of the areas listed. Refer to the text to explain the types of development to the parent or parents you are interviewing. Then compare the child's actual development with the usual development for three-year-olds described in the text.

| **Gross motor development** | **Fine motor development** |
|---|---|
| **Self-help skills** | **Language comprehension** |
| **Expressive language skills** | **Math readiness** |
| **Social development** | **Emotional development** |

What usual developments of three-year-olds has this child not yet achieved? _____

_____

_____

_____

_____

In what ways has this child matured beyond the level of most three-year-olds?_____

_____

_____

_____

_____

# Self-Help Skills

Name _____

Date _____ Period_____

Read the following list of self-help skills. Write two **(2)** beside each skill that is usually mastered by a two-year-old and three **(3)** beside each skill that is usually mastered by a three-year-old.

_____ 1. Opens snaps and zippers.

_____ 2. Gets through the night without wetting.

_____ 3. Works buckles.

_____ 4. Puts on shoes that do not tie.

_____ 5. Begins to cooperate in dressing.

_____ 6. Pours liquid from a small pitcher.

_____ 7. Removes socks, shoes, and pants.

_____ 8. Washes and dries face and hands.

_____ 9. Closes snaps.

_____ 10. Uses knife for spreading.

_____ 11. Pulls on simple garments.

_____ 12. Starts using the toilet when reminded.

_____ 13. Turns faucet on and off.

_____ 14. Has almost full control over toilet routines.

_____ 15. Unbuttons large buttons.

_____ 16. Seldom has bowel accidents.

# Language Skills

Name _____

Date _____ Period_____

Read the following list of language skills. Determine whether each is a language comprehension skill or an expressive language skill. Place a *C* in front of skills that are language comprehension. Place an *E* in front of skills that are expressive language skills.

_____  1. Combines two or more words such as "Boy hit."

_____  2. Understands and answers routine questions such as "What is your name?"

_____  3. Uses prepositions in speech.

_____  4. Follows three-part instruction.

_____  5. Points to six body parts on self or doll.

_____  6. Uses three-word sentences such as "You go home."

_____  7. Says "I want more cookies."

_____  8. Uses negative terms such as "Mommy don't go."

_____  9. Gives "just two" on request.

_____ 10. Understands the pronouns *you* and *they*.

_____ 11. Uses possessives such as "Mommy's coat."

_____ 12. Understands *smaller*.

_____ 13. Understands *larger*.

_____ 14. Provides appropriate answers for *how* questions.

_____ 15. Joins two sentences with a conjunction.

# Understanding Four- and Five-Year-Olds  6

## The Truth About Preschoolers

**Activity A**                             **Name** _____

**Chapter 6**                     **Date** _____ **Period** _____

Read the following statements. Circle *T* if the statement is true or *F* if the statement is false.

T   F   1.   Four- and five-year-olds usually express their anger by hitting other children.

T   F   2.   Verbal jokes are easy to understand for most four-year-olds.

T   F   3.   Some preschoolers begin losing their baby teeth.

T   F   4.   In a passive voice sentence, the subject of the sentence is placed before the object.

T   F   5.   Imaginary playmates are normal among four- and five-year-olds.

T   F   6.   Most four-year-olds understand that a dime is worth more than a nickel.

T   F   7.   Articulation is the ability to speak in clearly pronounced sounds.

T   F   8.   Four- and five-year-olds draw objects exactly the way they see them.

T   F   9.   At five and one-half years, children have legs that are about one-third the length of their bodies.

T   F  10.   Children learn to use irregular verbs during this preschool stage.

T   F  11.   Asking a child to be a helper builds self-esteem.

T   F  12.   Four- and five-year-olds do not fully understand what is and is not dangerous.

T   F  13.   Few four- and five-year-olds can walk on a balance beam.

T   F  14.   Most four- and five-year-olds are able to read.

T   F  15.   At age five, children use words related to ideas or thought in their daily language.

T   F  16.   Four- and five-year-olds prefer to have friends of the same sex.

T   F  17.   True counting usually comes before rote counting.

T   F  18.   Preschool children tend to talk to you rather than have a conversation with you.

T   F  19.   Four- and five-year-olds are not yet able to understand passive voice sentences.

T   F  20.   The writing and drawing skills of four- and five-year-olds improve quickly.

T   F  21.   Preschoolers tend to take literally statements that have more than one meaning.

T   F  22.   Asking questions is a way children try to make sense of their world.

T   F  23.   Stuttering usually results when a preschooler talks faster than he or she can think.

T   F  24.   Rote counting is reciting numbers in their proper order.

T   F  25.   Four- and five-year-olds may become reckless in working to improve their physical skills.

T   F  26.   Five-year-olds have a vocabulary of about 2000 words.

T   F  27.   By four years of age, most children use a fork to cut large pieces of food.

# Reading and Math Fun

Name _____

Date _____ Period_____

Using people or written materials as references, locate one rhyme, song, or game that could be used to develop reading skills and one rhyme, song, or game that could be used to develop math skills. Write the rhyme, song, or a description of the game in the space provided. Then tell what specific skills the activity will promote. Demonstrate both activities for the class.

**Reading Activity**

Skills this activity will promote: _____

_____

_____

_____

_____

_____

_____

*(Continued)*

**Math Activity**

Skills this activity will promote: _____
_____
_____
_____
_____
_____
_____

# Handling Emotions

Name _____

Date _____ Period_____

Read a current magazine article on helping preschoolers cope with such emotions as fear, anger, jealousy, or sadness. Summarize the article in the space provided. Present your report orally to the class.

Article Title: _____

Author: _____

Source: _____

Summary: _____

_____

_____

_____

_____

_____

_____

_____

_____

_____

_____

_____

_____

_____

_____

_____

_____

_____

_____

_____

_____

_____

_____

_____

_____

# Developing Activities

Name _____

Date _____ Period_____

Think of one original activity a teacher could use to help four- and five-year-olds in each area of development listed below. Describe the activities in the space provided and share them with others in the class.

Gross motor development: _____

_____

_____

_____

_____

_____

_____

_____

_____

_____

Fine motor development:_____

_____

_____

_____

_____

_____

_____

_____

_____

_____

_____

Language comprehension:_____

_____

_____

_____

_____

_____

_____

_____

*(Continued)*

**Name** _____

Expressive language: _____
_____
_____
_____
_____
_____
_____
_____

Math skills: _____
_____
_____
_____
_____
_____
_____
_____
_____

Social development: _____
_____
_____
_____
_____
_____
_____
_____
_____

Emotional development: _____
_____
_____
_____
_____
_____
_____
_____
_____

# Middle Childhood

**7**

## Understanding Middle Childhood Terms

**Activity A**

**Chapter 7**

Name _____

Date _____ Period_____

Match the following terms and definitions by placing the correct letters in the corresponding blanks.

_____ 1. Span of years between age 6 and 12.

_____ 2. Ability to see objects in a distance more easily than those that are close by.

_____ 3. Ability to see close objects more clearly than those at a distance.

_____ 4. Using logic but basing it on what has been seen or experienced.

_____ 5. Excessive body fat.

_____ 6. Technique children often use to remember information.

_____ 7. Manipulation of ideas based on logic rather than perception.

_____ 8. Ability to arrange items in increasing or decreasing order based on volume, size, or weight.

_____ 9. Change in position or shape of substances does not change the quantity.

_____ 10. Ability to group items by common attributes.

_____ 11. Process where people define themselves in terms of qualities, skills, and attributes they see in others.

_____ 12. Belief that you are a worthwhile person.

_____ 13. Ability to understand the feelings of others.

_____ 14. Being aware of others' distress and wanting to help them.

_____ 15. Understanding and using accepted rules of conduct when interacting with others.

_____ 16. The process of acquiring the standards of behavior considered acceptable by society.

A. moral development

B. farsighted

C. operation

D. classification

E. self-esteem

F. middle childhood

G. obesity

H. rehearsal

I. social comparison

J. empathy

K. nearsighted

L. seriation

M. conservation

N. morality

O. compassion

P. concrete operations

# Check Your Gender IQ

Name _____

Date _____ Period_____

The text describes many differences in physical development and social behavior between boys and girls during the school-age years. Read the following statements. In the blank before each statement, write **G** if the statement generally describes girls and **B** if the statement generally describes boys. Then try to observe school-age children during a school recess period and answer the questions at the end of this activity.

_____ 1. Taller at the beginning of this stage.

_____ 2. Tend to occupy space closer to the school building.

_____ 3. Are more open than secretive in their relationships.

_____ 4. Interact in pairs or small groups.

_____ 5. Best at skills requiring balance, flexibility, or rhythm.

_____ 6. Reach 80 percent of adult height by the end of middle childhood.

_____ 7. Play involves more taking turns and cooperating with others.

_____ 8. Experience a growth spurt at age 12.

_____ 9. Have more physical strength.

_____ 10. Prefer jumping rope and doing tricks on the jungle gym.

_____ 11. Tend to control large fixed spaces at school that are used for team sports.

_____ 12. Weigh more by 12 years of age.

_____ 13. Experience a growth spurt at age 10.

_____ 14. Prefer competitive sports.

Observe a large group of school-age children of the same age during a school recess period. Look for the gender differences listed above. Then answer the questions below.

1. Which of the above characteristics about boys were you able to observe?

   _____

   _____

   _____

2. Which of the above characteristics about girls were you able to observe?

   _____

   _____

   _____

3. It is important that early childhood teachers do not reinforce gender-role stereotypes. However, gender differences do exist among school-age children. How do you feel a teacher should respond to this dilemma?

   _____

   _____

   _____

   _____

# Health Dilemmas

Name _____

Date _____ Period _____

The situations below describe challenges you might face in handling health-related situations in the classroom. Break into small groups. Read each dilemma and discuss possible approaches to the situations. Write your group's best suggestions in the spaces provided.

1. You notice that Antwann, a seven year old, holds books four or five inches in front of his face. What might be his problem? What action should you take?

   _____

   _____

   _____

   _____

   _____

   _____

   _____

   _____

   _____

   _____

2. Toby's behavior is frustrating you. He seems to ignore most suggestions. After listening to a story, his responses to questions are inaccurate. What action should you take?

   _____

   _____

   _____

   _____

   _____

   _____

   _____

3. Rhonda is an obese child. At lunch and during snack time, she takes more food than needed. As her teacher, what can you do to help Rhonda with her weight problem? How would you suggest working with Rhonda's parents?

   _____

   _____

   _____

   _____

   _____

   _____

   _____

# Testing Mental Operations

Name _____

Date _____ Period_____

Children learn the concepts of conservation, seriation, and classification during the middle years. Design your own activities to test these concepts with a child between the ages of six and ten. After testing the child, record their responses below.

Age of child tested: _____

---

**Conservation**

Describe how you plan to test the child's understanding of the concept of conservation:

_____

_____

_____

What supplies will you need?_____

_____

What results do you expect that will show that the child understands conservation? _____

_____

_____

What were the results of your test with the child?_____

_____

_____

---

**Seriation**

Describe how you plan to test the child's understanding of the concept of seriation:_____

_____

_____

_____

What supplies will you need?_____

_____

What results do you expect that will show that the child understands seriation? _____

_____

_____

What were the results of your test with the child?_____

_____

_____

*(Continued)*

**Classification**

Describe how you plan to test the child's understanding of the concept of classification: _____

_____

_____

_____

What supplies will you need?_____

_____

What results do you expect that will show the child understands classification? _____

_____

_____

What were the results of your test with the child?_____

_____

_____

_____

_____

_____

# Beliefs About Middle Childhood

**Activity E**

**Chapter 7**

Name _____

Date _____ Period_____

Read each sentence and circle the word choice that best describes your beliefs. Then explain your answer in the space provided.

1. I believe friendships take on a **lesser/greater** importance in middle childhood than before.

   Reason: _____

   _____

   _____

   _____

2. I believe teachers **can/cannot** play an important role in building a school-age child's self-esteem.

   Reason: _____

   _____

   _____

   _____

3. I believe children **should be/should not be** encouraged to participate in team sports and competition during middle childhood.

   Reason: _____

   _____

   _____

   _____

4. I believe playing games that involve rules **is/is not** important to a school-age child's development.

   Reason: _____

   _____

   _____

   _____

# Preparing the Environment

## Meeting the Goals of a Well-Planned Space

**Activity A**

**Chapter 8**

Name _____

Date _____ Period_____

Pretend that you have been hired as the director of a new child care center. You have been asked to provide input into the design of the physical space. For each of the goals for a well-planned space listed below, give two examples of how you would meet that goal in designing the physical space.

**Goal 1:** To provide a physically safe environment for the children.

_____

_____

_____

**Goal 2:** To provide children with areas that promote cognitive, emotional, social, and physical growth.

_____

_____

_____

**Goal 3:** To provide adults with a space that is easy to supervise.

_____

_____

_____

**Goal 4:** To provide space that is pleasing to the eye for both adults and children.

_____

_____

_____

**Goal 5:** To provide easy access to materials when needed so children are able to direct themselves.

_____

_____

_____

**Goal 6:** To encourage children to take part in activities.

_____

_____

# Responses to Color

Name _____

Date _____ Period_____

Read the name of each color listed. In the space provided, record your responses to each color. Then ask a preschool child to share his or her thoughts about each color. Record the child's responses. Answer the questions below the chart to note similarities and differences in the responses.

| Color | My Thoughts | A Preschool Child's Thoughts |
|---|---|---|
| **Red** | | |
| **Blue** | | |
| **Green** | | |
| **Yellow** | | |
| **Purple** | | |
| **Pink** | | |
| **Black** | | |
| **Brown** | | |

What similarities and differences did you find in the responses? _____

_____

_____

_____

_____

_____

What might be some reasons for the differences? _____

_____

_____

_____

_____

_____

# Activity Areas

Name _____

Date _____ Period _____

List ten basic activity areas found in most classrooms. Name their functions and describe where each should be placed in the classroom.

1. _____
   _____
   _____
   _____

2. _____
   _____
   _____
   _____

3. _____
   _____
   _____
   _____

4. _____
   _____
   _____
   _____

5. _____
   _____
   _____
   _____

6. _____
   _____
   _____

7. _____
   _____
   _____

8. _____
   _____

*(Continued)*

9. _____

_____

_____

_____

10. _____

_____

_____

_____

Planning the outdoor play area is just as important as planning the indoor classroom areas. Answer the following questions about outdoor play areas.

11. List three guidelines for the best use of play yard space.

_____

_____

_____

_____

12. What are nine other items to consider when planning an outdoor play yard?

_____

_____

_____

_____

_____

_____

_____

_____

# Selecting Toys, Equipment, and Educational Materials

## Toys Meeting Goals

Name _____

Date _____ Period_____

Listed below are two program goals for a group of three-year-olds. Read the goals and available toys and equipment. Then list additional toys and equipment that are needed to help meet the program goals.

| Program Goals | Available Toys and Equipment | Toys and Equipment Needed |
|---|---|---|
| Goal A: To encourage language development. | *Books* | |
| Goal B: To encourage fine motor development. | *Puzzles* | |

Think of two or more possible program goals for a group of three-year-olds. List the program goals and toys that could help meet those goals.

| Program Goals | Toys and Equipment Needed |
|---|---|
| Goal A: | |
| Goal B: | |

# Age Appropriate Equipment

Name _____

Date _____ Period_____

Not all toys and equipment are appropriate for children of all ages. While some toys are suitable for infants, other toys are only appropriate for older children. Match the toys and equipment listed below with the age of the youngest children who should use them. Refer to Chart 9-8 in the text if necessary.

_____ 1. Activity gym.

_____ 2. Roller skates.

_____ 3. Cloth books.

_____ 4. Wooden telephone.

_____ 5. Tricycle.

_____ 6. Doll bed.

_____ 7. Play dough.

_____ 8. Small jungle gym.

_____ 9. Blunt scissors.

_____ 10. Pull toys.

_____ 11. Large wooden threading beads.

_____ 12. Giant dominoes.

_____ 13. Hard books.

_____ 14. Stacking and nesting toys.

_____ 15. Blunt scissors.

_____ 16. Walking board.

_____ 17. Scooter.

_____ 18. Coaster wagon.

_____ 19. Doll carriage.

_____ 20. Simple climber and slide.

A. six-month to one-year-old

B. one-year-old

C. two-year-old

D. three-year-old

E. four-year-old

F. five-year-old

# Actions to Take

Name _____

Date _____ Period_____

List an action you could take to improve the safety and performance of the toys and equipment listed below. Some items may need to be discarded.

| Condition or Toy to Improve | Action to Take |
| --- | --- |
| 1. Chipped paint. | |
| 2. Worn varnish. | |
| 3. Loose nuts. | |
| 4. Rusty equipment. | |
| 5. Squeaky bicycle wheels. | |
| 6. Broken plastic toy. | |
| 7. Play iron with cord and plug. | |
| 8. Toy gun. | |

*(Continued)*

| Condition or Toy to Improve | Action to Take |
|---|---|
| 9. War game. | |
| 10. Pull toy with small beads inside. | |
| 11. Swing seat with open S-ring. | |
| 12. Stuffed animal with button eyes. | |
| 13. Balloons. | |
| 14. Wooden swing seat. | |
| 15. Exposed screws and bolts. | |

# Comparing Prices

Name _____

Date _____ Period_____

Find the price charged for each of the following items by three different sources. For instance, check prices using Web sites, catalogs, stores, and co-ops. You might also try to check prices of secondhand equipment. Record each price and the source of your information in the space provided. Also record any other notes you want to remember about that source.

## Easel

| Vendor 1: | Vendor 2: | Vendor 3: |
|---|---|---|
| _____ | _____ | _____ |
| Price (including any shipping costs:) | Price (including any shipping costs:) | Price (including any shipping costs:) |
| _____ | _____ | _____ |
| Other important notes: | Other important notes: | Other important notes: |
| _____ | _____ | _____ |
| _____ | _____ | _____ |

## Sensory Table

| Vendor 1: | Vendor 2: | Vendor 3: |
|---|---|---|
| _____ | _____ | _____ |
| Price (including any shipping costs:) | Price (including any shipping costs:) | Price (including any shipping costs:) |
| _____ | _____ | _____ |
| Other important notes: | Other important notes: | Other important notes: |
| _____ | _____ | _____ |
| _____ | _____ | _____ |

## Tricycle

| Vendor 1: | Vendor 2: | Vendor 3: |
|---|---|---|
| _____ | _____ | _____ |
| Price (including any shipping costs:) | Price (including any shipping costs:) | Price (including any shipping costs:) |
| _____ | _____ | _____ |
| Other important notes: | Other important notes: | Other important notes: |
| _____ | _____ | _____ |
| _____ | _____ | _____ |

*(Continued)*

## Bookshelf

| Vendor 1: | Vendor 2: | Vendor 3: |
|---|---|---|
| _____ | _____ | _____ |
| Price (including any shipping costs:) | Price (including any shipping costs:) | Price (including any shipping costs:) |
| _____ | _____ | _____ |
| Other important notes: | Other important notes: | Other important notes: |
| _____ | _____ | _____ |
| _____ | _____ | _____ |

## Autoharp®

| Vendor 1: | Vendor 2: | Vendor 3: |
|---|---|---|
| _____ | _____ | _____ |
| Price (including any shipping costs:) | Price (including any shipping costs:) | Price (including any shipping costs:) |
| _____ | _____ | _____ |
| Other important notes: | Other important notes: | Other important notes: |
| _____ | _____ | _____ |
| _____ | _____ | _____ |

## 12 Cans Tempera Paint

| Vendor 1: | Vendor 2: | Vendor 3: |
|---|---|---|
| _____ | _____ | _____ |
| Price (including any shipping costs:) | Price (including any shipping costs:) | Price (including any shipping costs:) |
| _____ | _____ | _____ |
| Other important notes: | Other important notes: | Other important notes: |
| _____ | _____ | _____ |
| _____ | _____ | _____ |

Talk to people at two centers to learn whether the price quotations you received were realistic and whether a center could afford to pay those prices. Also ask for tips on how to obtain necessary equipment at the lowest possible cost. Record what you learn from these discussions.

_____

_____

_____

# Planning Nutritious Meals and Snacks

## Nutrients and Their Functions

**Activity A**          **Name** _____

**Chapter 11**          **Date** _____ **Period** _____

Match the following terms and identifying phrases.

_____ 1. Build and repair tissues.

_____ 2. Supplies energy and carries fat-soluble vitamins.

_____ 3. Helps prevent night blindness.

_____ 4. Combines with proteins to make hemoglobin.

_____ 5. Helps cells use other nutrients.

_____ 6. Aids in blood clotting.

_____ 7. Promotes normal appetite and digestion.

_____ 8. Helps build bones and teeth.

_____ 9. Helps transport nutrients and waste.

_____ 10. Helps regulate many body processes.

_____ 11. Provide bulk in the form of cellulose (needed for good digestion).

_____ 12. Helps keep skin, tongue, and lips healthy.

_____ 13. Helps body fight infection.

_____ 14. Acts as antioxidant.

_____ 15. Helps keep adult bones healthy.

A. calcium

B. carbohydrates

C. fat

D. iron

E. niacin

F. phosphorus

G. proteins

H. riboflavin

I. thiamin

J. vitamin A

K. vitamin C

L. vitamin D

M. vitamin E

N. vitamin K

O. water

# Nutrition Crossword

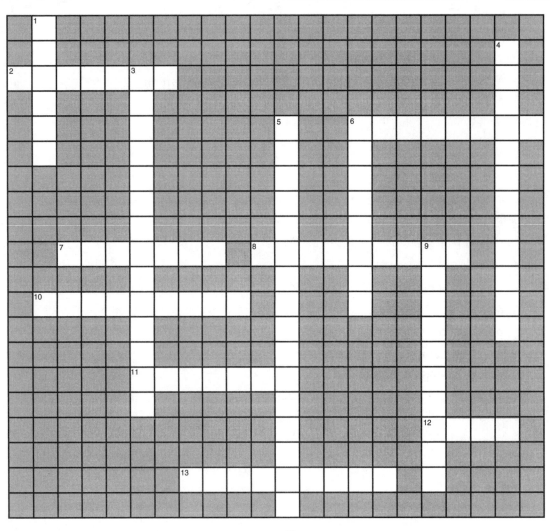

**Across**

2. The most important nutrient provided by the milk group is _____.
6. Deep yellow and dark green vegetables are rich sources of _____.
7. The most important nutrient supplied by the meat group is _____.
8. The science of food and how the body uses it is called _____.
10. Many milk products have been _____ to include vitamins A and D.
11. _____ is a condition that can lead to health problems such as hypertension in diabetes during adulthood.
12. The main sources of the mineral _____ are meat and meat alternates.
13. Chemical substances needed for growth and maintenance of health and found in foods are called _____.

**Down**

1. A child's diet should include six servings from the _____ group daily.
3. Not eating enough food to keep a healthy body weight and activity level is called _____.
4. _____ is a lack of nutrients in the diet.
5. Using the _____ for Young Children is an easy way to plan a nutritious diet.
6. Citrus fruits are rich sources of _____.
9. Taking in more food than the body needs to function properly is called _____.

# Food Guide Pyramid for Young Children

Name _____

Date _____ Period _____

A variety of food items are listed below. Place each of these items under the correct food group in the Food Guide Pyramid for Young Children.

| | | | |
|---|---|---|---|
| cottage cheese | apples | cheese | pea pods |
| collard greens | waffles | meatballs | crackers |
| kidney beans | granola | peanut butter | yogurt |
| chow mein noodles | broccoli | cheese fondue | dates |

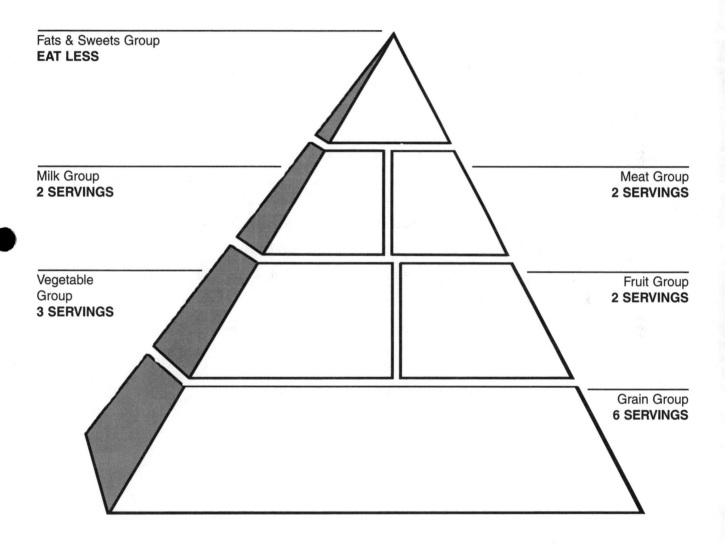

Fats & Sweets Group
**EAT LESS**

Milk Group
**2 SERVINGS**

Meat Group
**2 SERVINGS**

Vegetable Group
**3 SERVINGS**

Fruit Group
**2 SERVINGS**

Grain Group
**6 SERVINGS**

# Identifying the Sources

For each group of sources listed, fill in the blank with the name of the nutrient provided. Use each nutrient listed only once.

| | | |
|---|---|---|
| Carbohydrates | Fats | Niacin |
| Proteins | Riboflavin | Thiamin |
| Vitamin A | Vitamin C | Vitamin D |
| Vitamin E | Vitamin K | |

_____ 1. Egg yolk, organ meats, cauliflower, and leafy green vegetables.

_____ 2. Peanut butter, lentils, meat, poultry, fish, eggs, and dairy products.

_____ 3. Milk, cheese, yogurt, liver, meat, fish, poultry, and dark green leafy vegetables.

_____ 4. Breads, cereals, corn, peas, beans, potatoes, pasta, rice, fruits, vegetables, honey, sugar, jam, jelly, molasses.

_____ 5. Butter, cheese, cream, nuts, olives, chocolate, bacon, and salad oil.

_____ 6. Dark green and yellow fruits and vegetables, whole milk, butter, cream, fortified margarine, and cheeses.

_____ 7. Whole grain cereals, liver, eggs, fats, and leafy green vegetables.

_____ 8. Brewer's yeast, enriched or whole grain breads and cereals, dried beans, pork, and fish.

_____ 9. Sunshine, tuna, sardines, fish liver oils, liver, and fortified milk.

_____ 10. Tomatoes, cantaloupe, broccoli, and citrus fruits.

_____ 11. Dried beans, peas, whole grain cereals, fish, milk, poultry, and meat.

# Developing Guidance Skills 13

## Direct and Indirect Guidance

Name _____

Date _____ Period_____

Read each of the following statements and decide whether *direct* or *indirect* guidance is being described. Record your responses on the blank provided.

_____ 1. Removing a hot kettle from the cooking area.

_____ 2. Offering a child choices.

_____ 3. Telling a child what to do.

_____ 4. Lowering the easel so the children can comfortably reach the paper.

_____ 5. Moving a child's coat hook to a lower position in his or her locker.

_____ 6. Saying to a child, "Mary, you need to pick up that paper."

_____ 7. Telling Tom, "You'll lose your turn if you keep pushing."

_____ 8. Adding simple puzzles to the small manipulative area.

_____ 9. Providing a place mat with an outline of a glass, plate, spoon, and fork.

_____ 10. Suggesting to Wendy that she place her arm around Kris, who is crying.

_____ 11. Telling a child that her painting is beautiful.

_____ 12. Keeping your back to the wall so you can observe the entire classroom.

_____ 13. Reminding children to cover their mouths when they cough.

_____ 14. Placing a picture of the toy wagon on the shelf where it is stored.

_____ 15. Purchasing two additional scooters for the play yard since the scooter is a popular choice during free play.

_____ 16. Encouraging the children to work together by saying, "Ask Eve if she can help you."

_____ 17. Recognizing a child's accomplishment by saying, "I like the way you helped Amy."

_____ 18. Providing training scissors in the art area so Amanda can learn to cut.

_____ 19. Showing approval by smiling at Jamal after he finished a puzzle.

_____ 20. Seating Ethan and Chris apart during story time to prevent arguments.

# Positive Guidance

Name _____

Date _____ Period_____

Children are more likely to respond to positive statements than negative ones. Rewrite each statement below so it tells the child what he or she is expected to do.

1. "Don't put the scissors on the floor." _____
   _____

2. "Quit yelling." _____
   _____

3. "Don't spill your milk." _____
   _____

4. "Don't walk in front of the slide." _____
   _____

5. "You'll get water on your clothes." _____
   _____

6. "Don't spill sand." _____
   _____

7. "You're pouring too fast." _____
   _____

8. "Don't get the book dirty." _____
   _____

9. "Don't walk so slow." _____
   _____

10. "Don't touch all the muffins." _____
    _____

11. "Don't ride on the grass." _____
    _____

12. "You're hurting the bunny." _____
    _____

13. "Get off the gym." _____
    _____

14. "Don't eat the macaroni with your fingers." _____
    _____

# Putting Effective Guidance into Practice

Name _____

Date _____ Period_____

For each of the guidance techniques listed below, describe a situation where it would be appropriate to use. Then describe what you would do and say in each situation. Include all dialogue.

**Positive Reinforcement**

Describe the situation. _____

_____

_____

Describe how you would use positive reinforcement. _____

_____

_____

**Natural Consequences**

Describe the situation. _____

_____

_____

Describe how you would use natural consequences. _____

_____

_____

**Artificial Consequences**

Describe the situation. _____

_____

_____

Describe how you would use artificial consequences. _____

_____

_____

**I-Message**

Describe the situation. _____

_____

_____

Describe how you would use an I-message. _____

_____

_____

**Promoting a Positive Self-Concept**

Describe the situation. _____

_____

_____

Describe how you would use this situation to promote the child's self-concept._____

_____

_____

# Guidance Techniques

Name _____

Date _____ Period_____

Match each of the following statements to the letter of the guidance technique it illustrates. Then write an example of your own for each guidance technique listed.

_____ 1. "Sharon, paint only on your own paper. If you paint on Sandra's paper again, you'll have to move."

_____ 2. "Sally, let's draw on the chalkboard instead."

_____ 3. "Sue, what are the rules for using the jungle gym?"

_____ 4. "I liked the way you helped Kelsie."

_____ 5. "Wendy is having a temper tantrum. Pay no attention to her."

_____ 6. "Tommy, here is a paper towel."

_____ 7. "Peggy, I'm sorry. Here is a glass of juice."

_____ 8. "Lucia, I know you can do it!"

_____ 9. John said, "Steve won't give me play dough." The teacher repeated the statement. Then she added, "You're angry because Steve will not give you play dough."

_____ 10. "Use this pair of scissors. It does not have glue on its cutting edge, so it will cut easier."

A. ignoring

B. active listening

C. modeling

D. persuading

E. praising

F. prompting

G. encouraging

H. redirecting

I. suggesting

J. warning

1. _____
   _____

2. _____
   _____

3. _____
   _____

4. _____
   _____

5. _____
   _____

6. _____
   _____

7. _____
   _____

8. _____
   _____

9. _____
   _____

10. _____
    _____

## Guidance Match

**Activity A**                                          Name _____

**Chapter 14**                                          Date _____ Period_____

Match the terms in the right column with their descriptions in the left column.

_____  1. A form of body language used by very young children who cannot express themselves using words.

_____  2. Engaging in this activity in public is considered improper.

_____  3. This tension-relieving behavior usually peaks at 18 months.

_____  4. Many children experience this emotion on the first day of school.

_____  5. Used by insecure children as a way of getting attention.

_____  6. The larger the group, the greater the likelihood this state of overexcitement will occur.

_____  7. An external factor that affects each child differently.

_____  8. When children feel they are not in control, they may have these feelings of discouragement.

_____  9. Feelings of tensions that can be caused by both negative and positive events.

_____  10. Is common between two and three years of age as children attempt more independence.

A. biting

B. exploring the body

C. fear

D. frustration

E. negativism

F. noise

G. overstimulation

H. stress

I. thumbsucking

J. tattling

Choose one of the causes or reactions to tension listed above. Describe an instance where you observed this behavior in a young child. Explain how the adult (or you) handled the situation.

_____

_____

_____

_____

_____

_____

_____

_____

_____

_____

_____

# Guidance Tips

**Activity B**

**Chapter 14**

Name _____

Date _____ Period _____

Read the following statements related to guiding children. Circle *T* if the statement is true or *F* if the statement is false.

T  F  1. To avoid problems caused by noise, controlling the volume of tapes, records, and CDs works well.

T  F  2. Increasing the volume of your voice will cause children's voices to become softer.

T  F  3. Preparing materials in advance can cut down on waiting time.

T  F  4. Providing several kinds of toys allows children to choose the activities that reflect their needs and interests.

T  F  5. When you notice a child is under stress, its good to remain close to the child and comfort him or her.

T  F  6. If children steal, it is best to lecture them.

T  F  7. On certain occasions, young children should be allowed to hit each other.

T  F  8. Aggression can be relieved by yelling, beating drums, dancing to loud music, crying, and making animal noises.

T  F  9. Children who bite should be bitten back.

T  F  10. It is better to ignore thumbsucking than to pressure children to stop.

T  F  11. Children often need to act out situations to conquer their fears.

T  F  12. When children are afraid, they sometimes hit.

T  F  13. Children need to be alerted to changes in activities or routines well in advance.

T  F  14. It may be necessary to speed children along so the class activities remain on schedule.

T  F  15. You should suggest that an aggressive child sit down and look at a book.

T  F  16. A positive event, such as a new pet, can cause stress.

T  F  17. A sudden change in a child's behavior can be a bad sign of stress.

T  F  18. Instead of ignoring tattling behavior, you should speak to the child who has broken the rule.

T  F  19. Overstimulation, changes in routine, and loud noises can cause tension in young children.

T  F  20. Overstimulation is more common with a small group of children than with a large group.

T  F  21. Children usually demonstrate positive behavior when asked to wait for a long time.

T  F  22. The most common age for negativism is between four and five years.

T  F  23. To prevent tattling, you should work to build the child's self-esteem.

T  F  24. Children may reject a person or situation that feels strange or unsafe.

# Family Stressors Affect Guidance

Name _____

Date _____ Period_____

Interview a child care teacher using the questions below. Ask the teacher how family stressors affect the behavior of the children in his or her care. Record the teacher's responses in the space provided.

Teacher's Name and Program Name: _____

Age of children taught: _____

1. What family stressors have you noted among the children in your classroom? Please provide as many examples as you can with respect for confidentiality._____

   _____

   _____

2. Think of one particular instance. What behavioral changes did you observe in the child? _____

   _____

   _____

3. Did parents alert you to the stressor or did you first mention to them the behavioral changes you observed? Describe this interaction._____

   _____

   _____

   _____

4. What did you and the parents do to stop the resulting behavioral problems? How effective were these actions? _____

   _____

   _____

   _____

5. In what ways did you increase support to the child? _____

   _____

   _____

6. What did you learn from the experience?_____

   _____

   _____

   _____

# Dialing for Answers

Name _____

Date _____ Period_____

In the following exercise, the numbers below the blanks represent letters on the telephone dial. Use the clues and numbers to complete the following statements relating to guidance problems.

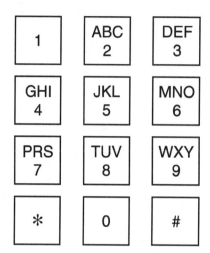

1. Guidance problems often occur in the form of __ __ __ __ __ __ __ __ __ __ behavior.
   3  4  7  7  8  7  8  4  8  3

2. __ __ __ __ __ __ __ __ __ __ __ can create tensions and cause children to feel they are not in control.
   3  7  8  7  8  7  2  8  4  6  6

3. Behavior can be affected by poor or inadequate __ __ __ __ __ __ __ __ __.
   6  8  8  7  4  8  4  6  6

4. One cause of __ __ __ __ __ __ for children is the breakup of a family.
   7  8  7  3  7  7

5. To help reduce stress, promote a __ __ __ __ __ __ __ __ environment.
   7  6  7  4  8  4  8  3

6. Between two and three years of age, preschool children can be __ __ __ __ __ __ __ __.
   6  3  4  2  8  4  8  3

7. The greatest number of __ __ __ __ __ __ __ __ usually occurs at about 18 months of age.
   8  2  6  8  7  8  6  7

8. Young children should never be allowed to __ __ __ other children.
   4  4  8

9. It is not unusual behavior for a two-year-old to __ __ __ __.
   2  4  8  3

10. __ __ __ __ __ __ __ __ __ __ __ __ __ is a tension-relieving behavior.
    8  4  8  6  2  7  8  2  5  4  6  4

## Stating the Positive

**Activity A**

**Chapter 15**

Name _____

Date _____ Period _____

Limits should be stated in a language the children can understand. They should also be simple, short, and positive. Limits should always give the children direction. State the following limits positively, telling the children what to do.

| Example limit | Limit rewritten in positive form |
|---|---|
| 1. Don't stand on the slide. | |
| 2. Don't leave the spills. | |
| 3. Don't leave the puzzle on the floor. | |
| 4. Don't tear the pages of the book. | |
| 5. Don't run in the classroom. | |

# Limit Pyramid

Name _____

Date _____ Period_____

Fill the pyramid with the words that are missing from the limits.

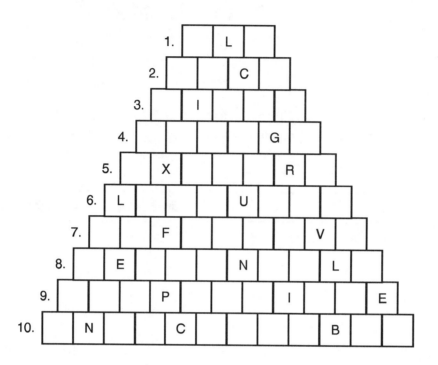

1. _____ employees should have a copy of classroom limits.

2. When a child is _____, the child may need more time to meet the demands of the teacher.

3. Every _____should be stated in a specific and positive way.

4. Any _____ in limits should always be discussed with the staff.

5. Children feel freer to _____ when they know their teacher will stop them if they go too far.

6. Limits should be written in a _____ children understand.

7. _____ limits serve as a kind of shorthand that state the goals of the center.

8. Limits that are not _____ can cause young children to feel angry.

9. Teachers are _____ for suggesting new limits to the director and staff.

10. _____ behavior needs to be stopped.

# Know the Limits

Activity C

Name _____

Chapter 15

Date _____ Period_____

Circle *T* if the statement is true or *F* if the statement is false.

T   F   1.  Limits are necessary only on the playground.

T   F   2.  The director's responsibility is to consistently maintain classroom limits.

T   F   3.  A copy of the limits should be posted on the bulletin board in the teacher's lounge and/or in the classroom.

T   F   4.  Limits help children develop self-control.

T   F   5.  Limits should be stated negatively, in terms of behavior to avoid.

T   F   6.  Unreasonable limits can cause young children to feel angry.

T   F   7.  All limits should have a useful function.

T   F   8.  Limits need to be re-examined on a regular basis by the entire staff.

T   F   9.  When a limit no longer fits the group's needs, it should be discarded.

T   F  10.  Unacceptable behavior should be stopped firmly and quickly.

T   F  11.  Limits need to be inflexible.

T   F  12.  Depending upon the material being used for sensory play, limits may change somewhat.

T   F  13.  Children must wash their hands before participating in a cooking activity.

T   F  14.  Limits in the art area are usually minimal.

T   F  15.  Teachers need to demonstrate some of the limits in the science area.

Describe what you think might happen if a center did not have limits. _____

_____

_____

_____

_____

_____

_____

_____

_____

_____

_____

_____

# Setting Limits

Name _____

Date _____ Period_____

Each of the areas in a center needs limits. Think of eight limits a center might have in addition to the limits discussed in the text and list them in the space provided. Indicate the area of the center to which each limit relates.

1. _____
   _____

2. _____
   _____

3. _____
   _____

4. _____
   _____

5. _____
   _____

6. _____
   _____

7. _____
   _____

8. _____
   _____

Visit a center and list five of its most important limits.

1. _____
   _____

2. _____
   _____

3. _____
   _____

4. _____
   _____

5. _____
   _____

How do the limits of the center compare with your limits and the limits discussed in the text?_____

_____

_____

_____

_____

_____

## Your Style of Managing Daily Routines

**Activity A**

**Chapter 16**

Name _____

Date _____ Period_____

Indicate whether you agree or disagree with the following statements about daily routines. Explain your answers in the space provided.

**Agree  Disagree**

_____ _____ 1. Children benefit from following a daily schedule.

_____

_____

_____

_____ _____ 2. Children gain satisfaction by doing things for themselves.

_____

_____

_____

_____ _____ 3. Teachers should always assist children.

_____

_____

_____

_____ _____ 4. Teachers should plan an activity during the arrival time to make the separation from parents easier.

_____

_____

_____

_____ _____ 5. Children should be responsible for hanging up their own coats.

_____

_____

_____

_____ _____ 6. Demonstrating at the child's eye level is the most effective.

_____

_____

_____

*(Continued)*

**Agree  Disagree**

_____ _____  7. Children should be required to tie their own shoes by age three.

_____

_____

_____

_____ _____  8. All children must nap.

_____

_____

_____

_____ _____  9. Four-year-old children should assist in setting the lunch table.

_____

_____

_____

_____ _____ 10. Children should be reprimanded when they spill milk.

_____

_____

_____

_____ _____ 11. Children should be served only one tablespoon of food for each year of age.

_____

_____

_____

_____ _____ 12. Snacks should be provided between meals for children who refuse to eat breakfast.

_____

_____

_____

_____ _____ 13. A dawdling child should be threatened.

_____

_____

_____

_____ _____ 14. Repeated vomiting should be ignored if you are sure the child is not ill.

_____

_____

_____

_____ _____ 15. Toilet learning should be required of children attending a preschool program.

_____

_____

_____

# Planning a Daily Schedule

Name _____

Date _____ Period_____

Working in a small group, plan a daily schedule for a child care center. Complete the form below as you develop your plans.

Group members: _____

Name of your child care center: _____

Age group and type of program you are offering (all-day, half-day, two-hour): _____

_____

General goals of your program: _____

_____

Fill in the schedule below, giving times, activities, procedures, and rationale for each time segment.

| Daily Schedule | | | |
|------|----------|------------|-----------|
| Time | Activity | Procedures | Rationale |
|  |  |  |  |
|  |  |  |  |
|  |  |  |  |
|  |  |  |  |
|  |  |  |  |
|  |  |  |  |
|  |  |  |  |
|  |  |  |  |
|  |  |  |  |
|  |  |  |  |
|  |  |  |  |
|  |  |  |  |
|  |  |  |  |
|  |  |  |  |
|  |  |  |  |
|  |  |  |  |
|  |  |  |  |
|  |  |  |  |
|  |  |  |  |
|  |  |  |  |

# Managing Conflicts

Name _____

Date _____ Period _____

Read each of the following situations. Then work in small groups to discuss them. Write a suggestion for solving each of the conflicts in a positive way.

1. Four-year-old Shyrell refuses to take off her coat. When she arrived at school, she went directly to the art area, picked up a paintbrush, and began to paint. How could you handle this situation?

   _____

   _____

   _____

   _____

2. Toby had a birthday last week. He is now four years old. He still depends on the teacher to help him put on his outdoor clothing. Will this cause Toby to become more dependent or more independent? What advice do you have for the teacher?

   _____

   _____

   _____

   _____

3. Sally does not appear to have an interest in food. Every day her teacher reminds her to eat during mealtime. Sally does not seem to take the teacher's advice. Sometimes the teacher even tries to feed Sally, but this does not appear to be effective. What advice do you have for Sally's teacher?

   _____

   _____

   _____

   _____

4. All children are expected to remain at the table until everyone is finished eating. However, Christine usually leaves the table before her peers have finished. So far her teacher has been ignoring this behavior. How may Christine's behavior affect the other children? What actions should Christine's teacher take?

   _____

   _____

   _____

   _____

5. After lying down on their cots at nap time, Rivka and Kato ask for a drink of water. This happens every day. Many times after they get water, the other children also request it. How can you prevent this from happening?

   _____

   _____

   _____

   _____

## Dog Flowchart

**Activity A**

**Chapter 17**

Name _____

Date _____ Period_____

Review the section on flowcharts in the text. Create a flowchart listing the possible concepts to be used in developing a theme on dogs. Then write objectives related to this theme.

```
┌─────────────────────┐
│                     │
│        Dogs         │
│                     │
└─────────────────────┘
```

Objectives:

1. _____

2. _____

3. _____

4. _____

5. _____

6. _____

# Learning Activities Related to a Theme on Dogs

Name _____

Date _____ Period_____

List below activities that you could use under each curriculum area for a theme focusing on dogs.

Art:

Storytelling:

Sensory Table:

Dramatic Play:

Music:

Science:

Math:

Fingerplays:

# Behaviors

**Activity C**

**Chapter 17**

Name _____

Date _____ Period_____

Check all the behaviors below that could be used in a lesson plan.

| | | | |
|---|---|---|---|
| _____ 1. weigh | _____ 15. lace | _____ 29. really understand |
| _____ 2. ask | _____ 16. color | _____ 30. name |
| _____ 3. catch | _____ 17. clap | _____ 31. throw |
| _____ 4. paint | _____ 18. think | _____ 32. tie |
| _____ 5. follow | _____ 19. taste | _____ 33. believe |
| _____ 6. know | _____ 20. roll | _____ 34. wipe off |
| _____ 7. climb | _____ 21. say | _____ 35. write |
| _____ 8. cut | _____ 22. collect | _____ 36. fully appreciate |
| _____ 9. remove | _____ 23. understand | _____ 37. locate |
| _____ 10. believe | _____ 24. turn | _____ 38. nail |
| _____ 11. feed | _____ 25. sit | _____ 39. tap |
| _____ 12. mark | _____ 26. appreciate | _____ 40. recognize |
| _____ 13. button | _____ 27. touch | |
| _____ 14. enjoy | _____ 28. stand | |

Select six of the behaviors you checked and use them to write learning objectives. Be sure your objectives include all three parts: the conditions of performance, the behavior, and the level of performance.

1. _____

   _____

2. _____

   _____

3. _____

   _____

4. _____

   _____

5. _____

   _____

6. _____

   _____

# Curriculum Building

Name _____

Date _____ Period_____

Fill in the squares with the correct terms.

| 1. | | | | | | | | | A | N | D | | | C | | | | — | | | | | | | | | | |
|---|---|---|---|---|---|---|---|---|---|---|---|---|---|---|---|---|---|---|---|---|---|---|---|---|---|---|---|
| 2. | | | | | | | | | | | | | U | | | | | | | | | | | | | | |
| 3. | | | | | | | | | | | | | R | | | | | | | | | | | | | | |
| 4. | | | | | | | | | | | | | R | | | | | | | | | | | | | | |
| 5. | | | | | | | | | | | | | I | | | | | | | | | | | | | | |
| 6. | | | | | | | | | | | | | C | | | | | | | | | | | | | | |
| 7. | | | | | | | | | | | | | U | | | | | | | | | | | | | | |
| 8. | | | | | | | | | | | | | L | | | | | | | | | | | | | | |
| 9. | | | | | | | | | | | | | U | | | | | | | | | | | | | | |
| 10. | | | | | | | | | | | | | M | | | | | | | | | | | | | | |
| 11. | | | | | | | | | | | | | B | | | | | | | | | | | | | | |
| 12. | | | | | | | | | | | | | U | | | | | | | | | | | | | | |
| 13. | | | | | | | | | | | | | I | | | | | | | | | | | | | | |
| 14. | | | | | | | | | | | | | L | — | | | | | | | | | | | | | |
| 15. | | | | | | | | | | | | | D | — | | | | | | | | | | | | | |
| 16. | | | | | | | | | | | | | I | | | | | | | | | | | | | | |
| 17. | | | | | | | | | | | | | N | | | | | | | | | | | | | | |
| 18. | | | | | | | | | | | | | G | | | | | | | | | | | | | | |

1. Approach to learning where learning is seen as a constant process of exploring and questioning.

2. Children who learn best through hearing.

3. Objectives that list what tools the child will use.

4. Objective that states the minimum standard of achievement.

5. Statements that describe the expected outcomes of an activity.

6. Overall view of the curriculum which outlines general plans.

7. Based on the concept that as children grow, their circle of interests becomes larger.

8. Outlines specific actions and activities that will be used to meet program goals.

9. Children who depend a great deal on sense of sight for learning.

10. Broad statements of purpose that reflect the end result of education.

11. Any visible activities done by the child.

12. How an activity will end.

13. Movement from one activity to another.

14. Children who prefer working alone and are often the first to try something new.

15. Children who like to work with others in groups and like to follow models when learning new activities.

16. How you will gain the children's attention.

17. Activities planned with a specific goal in mind.

18. Learning that occurs on the spur of the moment.

# A Sample Lesson

**Activity E**

**Chapter 17**

Name _____

Date _____ Period _____

Write a sample lesson plan for a group activity of your choice. Fill in the information requested in the space provided and share your plan with others in class.

Date: _____ Time: _____

Group: _____

Activity: _____

Goals: _____

_____

_____

_____

_____

_____

_____

Learning objectives: _____

_____

_____

_____

_____

_____

_____

Materials needed: _____

_____

_____

_____

_____

Motivation/introduction: _____

_____

_____

_____

_____

_____

*(Continued)*

Procedures: _____

_____

_____

_____

_____

_____

_____

Closure/transition: _____

_____

_____

_____

_____

Evaluation:_____

_____

_____

_____

_____

_____

# Guiding Art, Blockbuilding, and Sensory Experiences

**18**

## Stages of Artwork

**Activity A**

**Chapter 18**

Name _____

Date _____ Period_____

Match the following stages of art skill development with their description.

_____ 1. Occur between 15 months and 3 years of age.

_____ 2. Child attempts to mimic own view of the world.

_____ 3. Occur when the child is between three and four years of age.

_____ 4. Crudely drawn human figures are common.

_____ 5. Children do not make the connection between the marks on the paper and their own movements.

_____ 6. Occur during the fourth and fifth year.

_____ 7. Children learn basic forms such as ovals, rectangles, and circles.

_____ 8. First stage of artwork.

_____ 9. Children create symbols of people or objects they know.

_____ 10. Children are first able to control the size and shape of a line.

_____ 11. Children may begin to name their drawings.

_____ 12. Children produce their first real drawing.

_____ 13. The resulting art is merely a byproduct of the experience.

_____ 14. Cars, boats, and airplanes may appear in children's artwork.

_____ 15. Children first see the connection between their own movements and the marks they make on the page.

A. scribbles

B. basic forms

C. first drawings

# Characteristics of Children's Art

**Activity B**

**Chapter 18**

Name _____

Date _____ Period _____

Duplicate a child's artwork for each of the three stages listed. Indicate the appropriate ages for each stage and describe characteristics of the artwork.

| Scribbles | Age:<br>Characteristics of art: |
|---|---|
| **Basic Forms** | **Age:**<br>**Characteristics of art:** |
| **First Drawings** | **Age:**<br>**Characteristics of art:** |

# Sources of Free Art Materials

Activity C

Chapter 18

Name _____

Date _____ Period_____

Brainstorm a list of free materials that could be obtained from each of the following sources. Try to include at least five items that could be obtained from each source.

| Bakery | Doctor's office |
|---|---|
| _____ | _____ |
| _____ | _____ |
| _____ | _____ |
| _____ | _____ |
| _____ | _____ |
| **Bank** | **Eye doctor** |
| _____ | _____ |
| _____ | _____ |
| _____ | _____ |
| _____ | _____ |
| _____ | _____ |
| **Bookstore** | **Fabric store** |
| _____ | _____ |
| _____ | _____ |
| _____ | _____ |
| _____ | _____ |
| _____ | _____ |
| **Dentist** | **Florist** |
| _____ | _____ |
| _____ | _____ |
| _____ | _____ |
| _____ | _____ |
| _____ | _____ |
| **Grocery store** | **Newspaper/printer** |
| _____ | _____ |
| _____ | _____ |
| _____ | _____ |
| _____ | _____ |

*(Continued)*

| Hair stylist | Paint store |
|---|---|
| _____ | _____ |
| _____ | _____ |
| _____ | _____ |
| _____ | _____ |
| _____ | _____ |

| Jewelry store | Shoe store |
|---|---|
| _____ | _____ |
| _____ | _____ |
| _____ | _____ |
| _____ | _____ |
| _____ | _____ |

# Tips for Buying Art Supplies

Name _____

Date _____ Period_____

Pretend you are a director purchasing art supplies for your center. Next to each of the following items, indicate with a check mark whether you would purchase the item or acquire it through donations. If you plan to have the item donated, list possible sources in the community.

| Art Supplies | Purchase | Donate | Sources of Donations |
|---|---|---|---|
| Newsprint | | | |
| Wallpaper | | | |
| Fabric | | | |
| Plastic foam | | | |
| Packing materials | | | |
| Magazine pictures | | | |
| Buttons | | | |
| Cardboard | | | |
| Egg cartons | | | |
| Paper plates | | | |
| Chalk and crayons | | | |
| Scissors | | | |
| Glue and paste | | | |

# Rating Play Dough

**Activity E**

**Chapter 18**

Name _____

Date _____ Period_____

Prepare the three play dough recipes included in the text: refrigerator play dough, sawdust play dough, and cooked play dough. Rank them according to the criteria listed. Use a scale of 1 to 3 with 1 being the best rating. Total the scores for each play dough. The play dough with the lowest rating has the best score.

| | Stickiness | Softness | Odor | Texture | Visual Appeal | Keeping Quality | Total Score |
|---|---|---|---|---|---|---|---|
| **Refrigerator Play Dough**<br>General Reaction: | | | | | | | |
| **Sawdust Play Dough**<br>General Reaction: | | | | | | | |
| **Cooked Play Dough**<br>General Reaction: | | | | | | | |

Which play dough would you prefer to use in the classroom and why?

_____

_____

_____

_____

_____

# Guiding Storytelling Experiences

## Storytelling

**Activity A**

**Chapter 19**

Name _____

Date _____ Period_____

Read the following statements about storytelling. Circle *T* if the statement is true or *F* if the statement is false.

T   F   1.   Book reviews provide descriptions of books to avoid.

T   F   2.   Children can develop a love for stories and books as a result of daily storytelling experiences.

T   F   3.   Most preschool children can separate fact from fiction.

T   F   4.   Storytelling is a way to present information.

T   F   5.   Three-year-olds are usually ready for fantasy stories.

T   F   6.   It is important to have highly detailed illustrations for children.

T   F   7.   Social understanding is the theme of family life stories.

T   F   8.   Two-year-olds remain interested in a book for five to eight minutes.

T   F   9.   Three-year-olds are interested in books that contain many sentences on each page.

T   F   10.   Four-year-olds appreciate humor in books.

T   F   11.   *Little Red Riding Hood* would be an excellent book for a group of three- and four-year-olds.

T   F   12.   Oral reading skills can be developed by practicing in front of a mirror.

T   F   13.   You can set the mood for a story by making a personal comment.

T   F   14.   Whispering or shouting can add interest to a story.

T   F   15.   If children do not appear to like a story, talking faster may help.

T   F   16.   Speaking too slowly when storytelling is a common problem.

T   F   17.   A clear ending to a story is not necessary if children are paying attention.

T   F   18.   Draw-and-tell stories may be prepared so they can be used more than once.

T   F   19.   If you lack drawing skills, you should not use flipcharts.

T   F   20.   Keeping books and art supplies in the same area is a good way to conserve space.

# Choosing Books for Children

Name _____

Date _____ Period_____

Pretend you are writing a column for a parents' magazine. Next to each of the following ages, list tips for selecting books.

| Children's Age | Tips for Selecting Books |
|---|---|
| Birth to two years of age | |
| Two years of age | |
| Three years of age | |
| Four years of age | |
| Five years of age | |

# Story Comparisons

Name _____

Date _____ Period_____

Select three books that a teacher might read to children in a certain age group and compare the books in the chart provided.

Age group selected: _____

|  | **Book #1** | **Book #2** | **Book #3** |
|---|---|---|---|
| Book title: | | | |
| Description of book: | | | |
| Props that could be used in telling story: | | | |
| Positive features of book: | | | |
| Negative features of book: | | | |
| Concluding comments: | | | |

# Evaluate Your Storytelling Technique

Name _____

Date _____ Period_____

Choose a partner. Select a book to read to a small group of children. Have your partner watch and evaluate you using the following checklist. Then evaluate your partner using the same checklist. Answer the questions that follow.

| Excellent | Good | Needs Improvement | |
|---|---|---|---|
| _____ | _____ | _____ | 1. Chose a developmentally-appropriate book for the children. |
| _____ | _____ | _____ | 2. Used a good introduction to establish the mood of the story. |
| _____ | _____ | _____ | 3. Explained unfamiliar words. |
| _____ | _____ | _____ | 4. Encouraged child participation. |
| _____ | _____ | _____ | 5. Told the story with a conversational tone. |
| _____ | _____ | _____ | 6. Used eye contact. |
| _____ | _____ | _____ | 7. Conveyed enthusiasm. |
| _____ | _____ | _____ | 8. Demonstrated good posture. |
| _____ | _____ | _____ | 9. Used different voices for particular characters to create interest. |
| _____ | _____ | _____ | 10. Pronounced words clearly. |
| _____ | _____ | _____ | 11. Used a lively tempo. |
| _____ | _____ | _____ | 12. Allowed children to add comments to the story. |
| _____ | _____ | _____ | 13. Held the book in a way that allowed children to see the pictures. |

What are your strengths?_____

_____

What are your weaknesses? _____

_____

What steps can you take to improve your skills? _____

_____

_____

_____

_____

# Guiding Play and Puppetry Experiences

## Playtime Match

Match the following terms and definitions by placing the correct letters in the corresponding blanks.

_____ 1. Commenting to children who follow desired behavior.

_____ 2. Contains materials and equipment that encourages children to explore roles.

_____ 3. Form of social play in which several children play together as they imitate others.

_____ 4. The third stage of material use in play that occurs when children do not need realistic props to play.

_____ 5. Play between two or more children.

_____ 6. Children play by themselves, but stay close to other children.

_____ 7. Occurs when the teacher shows the correct behavior for children during their socio-dramatic play.

_____ 8. Form of play in which a child imitates others.

_____ 9. Giving human traits to nonliving objects.

_____ 10. Two or more forces that oppose each other.

_____ 11. Skill that requires the teacher to provide children with ideas for difficult situations.

_____ 12. Type of play that allows a child to imitate others while using puppets in play.

_____ 13. The second stage of material use that occurs when children use props as intended while playing with other children.

_____ 14. Form of play in which children play alone without involving other children.

_____ 15. Occurs when a child displaces his or her emotions onto an object.

_____ 16. Type of play in which children mimic various adult roles.

_____ 17. The first stage of material use which occurs when children handle the props they are given.

_____ 18. Figure designed in likeness to an animal or human.

A. prop box

B. coaching

C. conflict

D. cooperative play

E. dramatic play

F. reinforcing

G. functional stage

H. imaginative stage

I. manipulative stage

J. modeling

K. parallel play

L. personification

M. projection

N. puppet

O. puppetry

P. role-playing

Q. socio-dramatic play

R. solitary play

# Encouraging Socio-Dramatic Play

**Activity B**

**Chapter 20**

Name _____

Date _____ Period_____

Prop boxes are used to extend children's play. In the space below, list materials that could be included in a prop box for an office worker, painter, baker, and carpenter. Think of two other categories and list the materials that could be included in a prop box for each of those categories.

| Office Worker | Painter |
|---|---|
| **Baker** | **Carpenter** |
| | |

Describe several actions a teacher could take to encourage children to participate in socio-dramatic play.

_____

_____

_____

_____

_____

_____

_____

_____

_____

_____

_____

# Design a Puppet

Name _____

Date _____ Period _____

Design a puppet for use with preschool children. Answer the questions below.

1. What type of puppet are you designing? (hand, mascot, "me") _____

2. What is your puppet's name? _____

3. Sketch your design for the puppet:

4. List the materials you will need to create the puppet:

   _____    _____

   _____    _____

   _____    _____

   _____    _____

   _____    _____

5. In what area of the curriculum could this puppet be used? _____

   Give specific examples for its use: _____

   _____

   _____

   *(Continued)*

6. How could your puppet be used to learn more about what an individual child is thinking or feeling?_____

_____

_____

_____

7. Optional: If you are able to use your puppet with preschoolers, tell about your experience. How did you use the puppet? How did the children react to your puppet? _____

_____

_____

_____

_____

_____

_____

_____

_____

_____

# Writing Puppet Stories

Name _____

Date _____ Period_____

Reread the information on puppets in the chapter. Then write a puppet story. Begin with a theme and develop a plot. Use the space below to write the story.

Theme:_____

_____

_____

_____

Story: _____

_____

_____

_____

_____

_____

_____

_____

_____

_____

_____

_____

_____

_____

_____

_____

_____

_____

_____

_____

_____

*(Continued)*

Name _____

## Practice Your Writing

**Activity A**

**Chapter 21**

Name _____

Date _____ Period _____

Using Chart 21-4 for guidance, take out a separate sheet of paper and practice making the uppercase letters, lowercase letters, and numerals 1-9 using the proper techniques. When you are satisfied with your work, reproduce the chart on this page.

_____

_____

_____

_____

Explain several problems that children may have in the early stages of writing. _____

_____

_____

_____

As a teacher, what might you do to help these children? _____

_____

_____

# Manuscript Writing

Name _____

Date _____ Period_____

Read each description listed below and write the answer in the blank.

_____ 1. Another name for manuscript writing.

_____ 2. This type of coordination involves muscle control that allows the hand to do a task the way the eye sees it done.

_____ 3. This type of writing can be done more quickly than manuscript.

_____ 4. Writing requires use of the fingers and hands.

_____ 5. A difficult task for many beginning writers.

_____ 6. Type of line that may occur when children write too slowly.

_____ 7. This type of writing may be caused by a pencil that is too fine or too hard.

_____ 8. Common problem in which children write letters backwards.

_____ 9. The percentage of children who are left-handed.

_____ 10. Technique to use when a child is having difficulty writing a particular letter.

_____ 11. Letters that are half the size of capital letters in manuscript writing.

_____ 12. Another name for capital letters.

13. What materials can teachers display to encourage printing? _____

_____

_____

14. Name an activity you can use to help develop children's fine motor coordination._____

_____

_____

15. Name an activity you can use to help develop children's hand-eye coordination._____

_____

_____

# Guiding Math Experiences **22**

## Math Match

**Activity A**                          Name _____

**Chapter 22**                          Date _____ Period_____

Match the following math terms with their definitions.

_____  1. Groups of objects that are alike in some way and therefore belong together.

_____  2. Process of physically separating objects into categories based on unique features.

_____  3. A set with no members.

_____  4. Method of assessment that involves giving children set activities to determine skills and/or needs.

_____  5. Process of mentally grouping objects or ideas into categories based on some unique feature.

_____  6. Involves attaching a number to a series of grouped objects.

_____  7. Simple form of classification that allows children to join a new experience with a similar, earlier experience.

_____  8. Form of classification that involves putting like objects together.

_____  9. The recitation of numbers in order.

_____ 10. Blocks of varying colors and geometric shapes.

_____ 11. The understanding that one group has the same number as another.

_____ 12. Each of these number symbols represents a quantity.

A. classification

B. empty set

C. matching

D. numerals

E. one-to-one correspondence

F. parquetry blocks

G. rational counting

H. recognizing

I  rote counting

J. sets

K. sorting

L. specific task assessment

# Color, Shape, and Counting Concepts

Name _____

Date _____ Period_____

Young children will learn the math concepts of color, shape, and counting. As an early childhood teacher, you will be responsible for providing activities that help children explore these concepts. To gain some practice, create two activities to be used with young children for each concept.

## Color

1. Age of children for which the activity is designed: _____

   Materials needed: _____

   Description of activity: _____

   _____

   _____

2. Age of children for which the activity is designed: _____

   Materials needed: _____

   Description of activity: _____

   _____

   _____

## Shape

1. Age of children for which the activity is designed: _____

   Materials needed: _____

   Description of activity: _____

   _____

   _____

2. Age of children for which the activity is designed: _____

   Materials needed: _____

   Description of activity: _____

   _____

   _____

## Counting

1. Age of children for which the activity is designed: _____

   Materials needed: _____

   Description of activity: _____

   _____

   _____

2. Age of children for which the activity is designed: _____

   Materials needed: _____

   Description of activity: _____

   _____

   _____

# Teaching Space, Size, Volume, and Time

Name _____

Date _____ Period _____

Space, size, volume, and time are four math concepts that are important for young children to learn. Specific terms related to each of these concepts are listed on this page. Think of an original way you could teach children to understand these terms and explain your method in the space provided.

## Space Concepts

High and low: _____

_____

_____

_____

Here and there: _____

_____

_____

_____

Inside and outside: _____

_____

_____

_____

Top, center, and bottom: _____

_____

_____

## Size Concepts

Big and little: _____

_____

_____

_____

Wide and thin: _____

_____

_____

_____

Inches and pounds: _____

_____

_____

_____

Smaller than and bigger than: _____

_____

_____

*(Continued)*

**Name** _____

## Volume Concepts

Much:_____

_____

_____

_____

Empty:_____

_____

_____

_____

Full:_____

_____

_____

_____

Some:_____

_____

_____

_____

## Time Concepts

Day and night:_____

_____

_____

_____

Before and after:_____

_____

_____

_____

Now and later:_____

_____

_____

_____

New and old:_____

_____

_____

_____

# Using Recipes to Teach Math Concepts

Name _____

Date _____ Period _____

Look through a cookbook and find two recipes that could be used for cooking activities to teach children math concepts. Record the recipes in the space provided and answer the questions.

**Recipe:** _____

What mathematical concepts and terms could this cooking activity teach children? _____

_____

_____

_____

_____

How could children participate in this activity? _____

_____

_____

_____

_____

*(Continued)*

**Recipe:** _____

What mathematical concepts and terms could this cooking activity teach children? _____

_____

_____

_____

_____

How could children participate in this activity? _____

_____

_____

_____

_____

# Guiding Science Experiences 23

## Science Overview

**Activity A**

**Chapter 23**

Name _____

Date _____ Period_____

Answer the following questions about science and science activities.

1. What is science? _____
   _____
   _____

2. What do children learn from using their senses to observe? _____
   _____
   _____
   _____

3. How can children benefit from studying science? _____
   _____
   _____
   _____
   _____
   _____

4. Why is the science area best located near the kitchen? _____
   _____
   _____

5. What factors should you consider when selecting equipment and materials for the science area? _____
   _____
   _____
   _____

6. List ten items you might find on a science table. _____
   _____
   _____
   _____
   _____

*(Continued)*

7. What are the five basic process skills that science activities should promote? _____

   _____

   _____

   _____

   _____

   _____

8. Give an example of one way you can help children learn about each of the following senses.

   a. Feeling: _____

   _____

   _____

   b. Smelling: _____

   _____

   _____

   c. Seeing: _____

   _____

   _____

   d. Hearing: _____

   _____

   _____

   e. Tasting: _____

   _____

   _____

# Forming Open-Ended Questions

**Activity B**

**Chapter 23**

Name _____

Date _____ Period _____

For each closed-ended question given, write a related open-ended question you could ask instead.

1. What happens to the ice when we add heat?

   _____

2. Does a rabbit have fur?

   _____

3. Does the potato stay hard inside when we cook it?

   _____

4. Which object feels soft?

   _____

5. Which classroom pet has fins for swimming?

   _____

6. Does a bubble contain air?

   _____

7. Does the magnet attract the plastic lids?

   _____

8. Which item is a darker blue?

   _____

9. To boil an egg, what must we put in the pot first?

   _____

10. Who is the person in this picture?

    _____

11. Does the tricycle have three wheels?

    _____

12. Is soup warmer than pudding?

    _____

13. How many legs does the canary have?

    _____

14. Do magnets attract other magnets?

    _____

15. Is the sandpaper scratchy or smooth?

    _____

# Pet Care

Name _____

Date _____ Period_____

Read the following statements about pets and the care they require. Circle *T* if the statement is true or *F* if the statement is false.

T   F   1. Guinea pigs and rabbits eat similar foods.

T   F   2. Rabbits actually eat very little.

T   F   3. Guinea pigs need space in a cage to hide, exercise, and sleep.

T   F   4. A rabbit's cage needs to be cleaned often.

T   F   5. One strain of hamster spreads a form of meningitis.

T   F   6. Rabbits should have wood for gnawing.

T   F   7. Snakes should be placed in a wire rustproof cage.

T   F   8. Hamsters enjoy lettuce, clover, alfalfa, and grass.

T   F   9. Hamsters may bite when exposed to loud voices.

T   F   10. Newspaper should be spread on the floor of a snake's aquarium.

T   F   11. A pet shop salesperson or conservation authority worker can help you determine a snake's dietary needs.

T   F   12. The larger species of snakes eat frogs and mice.

T   F   13. Frogs can be housed in an aquarium.

T   F   14. Toads enjoy eating rabbit pellets.

T   F   15. Frogs enjoy small earthworms and insects.

T   F   16. Canned dog food may be fed to toads.

T   F   17. The pH balance can be made more acidic by adding sodium biphosphate.

T   F   18. You can place a wooden box in one end of a rabbit cage for shelter.

T   F   19. Cabbage and lettuce can be fed to fish.

T   F   20. When rabbits have eaten cabbage, their urine has a strong, unpleasant odor.

# Methods of Teaching Science

**Activity D**

**Chapter 23**

Name _____

Date _____ Period_____

You can use many objects, ideas, and events that are familiar to children to teach them science concepts. Listed below are the methods that were discussed in the chapter. List at least three science concepts that children could learn through each method of teaching.

1. Using color to teach science:_____

   _____

   _____

   _____

   _____

2. Using water to teach science: _____

   _____

   _____

   _____

   _____

3. Using foods to teach science: _____

   _____

   _____

   _____

   _____

4. Using the child's own body to teach science: _____

   _____

   _____

   _____

   _____

5. Using gardening to teach science:_____

   _____

   _____

   _____

   _____

6. Using air to teach science:_____

   _____

   _____

   _____

   _____

*(Continued)*

7. Using magnets to teach science: _____

_____

_____

_____

_____

8. Using wheels to teach science: _____

_____

_____

_____

_____

9. Using field trips to teach science: _____

_____

_____

_____

_____

10. Using animals to teach science: _____

_____

_____

_____

_____

# Guiding Social Studies Experiences

## Social Studies Activities

**Activity A**  Name _____

**Chapter 24**  Date _____ Period_____

The early childhood years are an ideal time for children to begin learning about social studies. Young children can develop concepts related to each of the areas listed below. Describe one activity or incidental learning that would help promote learning in each area.

1. Develop self-respect and a healthy self-concept. _____

_____

_____

_____

_____

2. Develop respect for other people. _____

_____

_____

_____

_____

3. Develop self-control and independence. _____

_____

_____

_____

_____

4. Learn to share ideas and materials. _____

_____

_____

_____

_____

5. Develop healthy ways of relating to and working with others._____

_____

_____

_____

_____

*(Continued)*

6. Gain the attitudes, knowledge, and skills needed for living in a democracy. _____

_____

_____

_____

_____

7. Develop respect for other people's feelings, ideas, and property. _____

_____

_____

_____

_____

8. Learn about the roles people have in life. _____

_____

_____

_____

_____

9. Learn to appreciate the past and its relationship to the present. _____

_____

_____

_____

_____

10. Learn the need for and importance of limits. _____

_____

_____

_____

_____

# Using a Theme in Planning

Name _____

Date _____ Period _____

Themes can be used to combine the learning opportunities of many different activities. Plan a social studies program around a theme of your choice. Describe several learning experiences for each of the activity areas listed.

| Theme: | |
|---|---|
| **Activity Area** | **Learning Experience** |
| Art | |
| Technology Center | |
| Book Center | |
| Games | |
| Fingerplay | |
| Gross Motor Activity | |
| Cooking and Snacks | |
| Dramatic Play | |
| Small Manipulative | |

# Know Your Resources

Name _____

Date _____ Period_____

Identify available community resources that may be helpful in planning a variety of learning opportunities. Record the names of stores, museums, art galleries, community services, community workers, housing groups, and other community resources that may be helpful. List the information or services that each group can provide you. The Yellow Pages of your local telephone book is a good place to begin looking for this information.

| Community Resources | Information/Services Provided |
|---|---|
| | |

## Teaching Nutrition

**Activity A**              Name _____

**Chapter 25**             Date _____ Period_____

Develop a colorful rebus chart that presents basic nutrition information. In a rebus chart, basic drawings, symbols, or pictures are used in place of the words they represent. For example, the drawing 👁 might replace the word *I*. Then describe how you would use this chart to explain the concepts to a group of young children.

How could you use this chart to explain nutrition concepts to a group of young children? _____

_____

_____

_____

# Collecting Recipes

Name _____

Date _____ Period _____

Research cookbooks and find two nutritious recipes that could be used with children. Write the recipes on the recipe cards provided. Beneath each recipe card, develop a recipe chart. Number each step on the chart and use very simple descriptions of the steps. Design the chart so young children will be able to follow along with your help.

**Recipe:** _____

**Recipe Chart**

*(Continued)*

**Recipe:** _____

**Recipe Chart**

# Setting the Table

Name _____

Date _____ Period _____

Design a place mat for teaching children how to set the table. Include a plate, glass, fork, spoon, and napkin. Draw your place mat in the space provided. You can turn the page horizontally if you wish.

## Musical Truths

**Activity A**

**Chapter 26**

Name _____

Date _____ Period_____

Read the following statements about music. Circle *T* if the statement is true or *F* if the statement is false.

T   F   1.   Music is a form of communication.

T   F   2.   Music can be used to teach children language skills.

T   F   3.   Music experiences can help children build positive self-concepts.

T   F   4.   The music area should be located in a small corner of the classroom.

T   F   5.   Music experiences should always be structured.

T   F   6.   Teachers need to have loud singing voices.

T   F   7.   Children respond better to spoken directions than to musical directions.

T   F   8.   Music activities should be set in a time and place.

T   F   9.   The best songs for young children have a strongly defined mood or rhythm.

T   F   10.   Adding new words to a known melody is an easy way to make a song.

T   F   11.   The whole song method is best for teaching long songs.

T   F   12.   The teacher's enthusiasm and enjoyment of music are more important than a polished musical performance.

T   F   13.   The Autoharp® has several advantages over a piano.

T   F   14.   The guitar is easier to play than the Autoharp®.

T   F   15.   Rhythm instruments can be used to accompany the beat of a recording.

T   F   16.   If possible, use seven or eight types of rhythm instruments at one time.

T   F   17.   Children of all ages can enjoy sandpaper blocks.

T   F   18.   The children can take part in making rattlers.

T   F   19.   Children need to be taught how to listen.

T   F   20.   Movement activities are most successful when the children are tired and irritable.

# Rhythm Instruments

Name _____

Date _____ Period_____

Choose one of the rhythm instruments listed below. Develop and perform a demonstration on how to make and use this instrument. Write your notes for the demonstration in the space provided.

sandpaper blocks          rattlers          tin can tom-toms
sandpaper sticks          shakers          coconut cymbals
bongo drums          rhythm sticks          jingle sticks
tom-tom drums          rhythm bells

Instrument to be used: _____

Notes for demonstration:_____

_____

_____

_____

_____

_____

_____

_____

_____

_____

_____

_____

_____

_____

_____

_____

_____

_____

_____

_____

_____

_____

_____

_____

_____

_____

# Fingerplays

Name _____

Date _____ Period_____

List two considerations for choosing a fingerplay for a two-year-old.

1. _____

2. _____

In the space provided, write an original fingerplay that you could teach to a two-year-old child. Include descriptions of the actions that go along with the words.

_____

_____

_____

_____

_____

_____

_____

_____

_____

_____

_____

_____

_____

_____

_____

_____

_____

_____

_____

_____

_____

_____

_____

_____

# Teaching Movement

Name _____

Date _____ Period _____

Resolve each situation below by providing an appropriate solution.

1. You are going to teach children to clap with their hands. How can you do this?

   _____

   _____

   _____

2. You are assigned to teach a movement activity. How can you prepare for this?

   _____

   _____

   _____

3. One of the first movement activities should focus on listening. What type of beat should you provide for two-year-olds?

   _____

   _____

   _____

4. Space awareness is part of the preschool curriculum. How can you teach this concept?

   _____

   _____

   _____

5. You have been assigned to teach a word game. What types of words should you use?

   _____

   _____

   _____

6. You are planning a pantomiming activity. For what age level would this activity be most suitable?

   _____

   _____

   _____

# Guiding Field Trip Experiences

## Community Field Trips

Activity A                          Name _____

Chapter 27                          Date _____ Period_____

List 10 specific field trips in your community that young children would enjoy. List the themes that relate to each trip.

| Field Trip | Related Themes |
|---|---|
| 1. | |
| 2. | |
| 3. | |
| 4. | |
| 5. | |
| 6. | |
| 7. | |
| 8. | |
| 9. | |
| 10. | |

# Planning the Trip

**Activity B**

**Chapter 27**

Name _____

Date _____ Period_____

Select one of the field trips from the list you created in Activity A. Fill in the information requested to make plans for the trip. Then trade your plans with another person and offer each other comments and suggestions for improving the plans.

Description of field trip selected: _____

_____

Age of children who will participate: _____

Number of children who will participate: _____

Number of adults who will help: _____

Ways children will learn through participation: _____

_____

_____

_____

_____

Total cost of the trip (including transportation, admission, food, etc.): _____

Time you will leave the center: _____

Approximate time you will return to the center: _____

Your educational goals for the trip: _____

_____

_____

_____

_____

How you will prepare the children for the trip: _____

_____

_____

_____

_____

Follow-up activities to reinforce learning: _____

_____

_____

_____

_____

_____

# Before and After the Field Trip

Name _____

Date _____ Period_____

The success of a field trip depends on how well the teacher prepares before the trip and follows up after the trip. Assume that you will be taking a group of children on a trip to the local post office. Brainstorm a list of specific pretrip preparations. Include plans you will make and information and questions to discuss with the tour guide prior to the field trip. Then brainstorm a list of follow-up activities to help children clarify their learning. Share your lists with others in the class.

| Pretrip Preparations | Follow-Up Activities |
|---|---|
|  |  |

# Completing the Trip

**Activity D**

**Chapter 27**

Name _____

Date _____ Period_____

Complete the following statements about field trips by filling in the blanks with the correct words.

| | | | |
|---|---|---|---|
| community | fall | observation | short |
| concepts | familiar | permission | social |
| crowds | file | preparation | theme |
| curriculum | follow-up | pretrip | tissues |
| directions | machinery | resource | value |

_____ 1. Field trips are an important part of the _____ for preschool children.

_____ 2. Field trips help children develop _____ skills.

_____ 3. Vague _____ become clearer to children as they gain new information.

_____ 4. By participating in field trips children learn about their _____.

_____ 5. Taking field trips helps children practice following _____.

_____ 6. A field trip to the farm may be chosen while children are studying about farms, food, or _____.

_____ 7. A trip to a pumpkin patch or apple orchard can be taken during the _____ season.

_____ 8. The first trips children take should be _____ and nonthreatening.

_____ 9. After taking trips around the neighborhood, field trips may be taken to _____ places.

_____ 10. _____ walks provide a chance to sharpen children's observation skills.

_____ 11. People walks can teach many _____ concepts.

_____ 12. You should keep a _____ on field trips.

_____ 13. The success of a trip depends on your _____.

_____ 14. You should take paper _____ and a first aid kit on the trip.

_____ 15. _____ slips must be signed by parents.

_____ 16. _____ may overwhelm some children.

_____ 17. Guests or field trip hosts are called _____ people.

_____ 18. After setting goals for the trip, always take a _____ if you have never been to the trip site.

_____ 19. To help children clarify what they have learned, plan _____ activities.

_____ 20. Follow-up activities will reinforce the _____ of the experience.

## Caregiver Traits

**Activity A**

**Chapter 28**

Name _____

Date _____ Period _____

Check all the traits listed that you feel an infant or toddler caregiver should model. Then go through the list again. This time check the traits you model. Answer the questions on the next page.

| Personal Traits | Traits a Caregiver Should Model | Traits I Model | Personal Traits | Traits a Caregiver Should Model | Traits I Model |
|---|---|---|---|---|---|
| cheerful | | | disinterested | | |
| forgetful | | | patient | | |
| self-confident | | | friendly | | |
| honest | | | shy | | |
| cooperative | | | warm | | |
| self-disciplined | | | cold | | |
| unconfident | | | concerned | | |
| curious | | | dependable | | |
| active | | | enthusiastic | | |
| nurturing | | | moody | | |
| smiling | | | pleasant | | |
| inflexible | | | helpful | | |
| consistent | | | respectful | | |
| reliable | | | predictable | | |
| well-organized | | | kind | | |
| trustworthy | | | understanding | | |
| courteous | | | responsive | | |
| unpredictable | | | easily distracted | | |

*(Continued)*

1. Compare your list of traits caregivers should model with the lists of others in the class. Did you choose the same traits? Why or why not? _____

   _____

   _____

   _____

   _____

   _____

2. In what general areas are you a model of positive traits? _____

   _____

   _____

   _____

   _____

   _____

3. In what areas can you improve? What can you do to improve? _____

   _____

   _____

   _____

   _____

   _____

4. Do you think a parent should model the same traits as a caregiver? Why or why not? _____

   _____

   _____

   _____

   _____

   _____

# Environment Needs

Name _____

Date _____ Period_____

For each of the following questions, select the best answer and write the letter in the blank. Then give an explanation for each answer in the space provided.

_____ 1. The diapering area should be located next to a(n) _____.

     A. entrance           B. sink

Reason: _____

_____

_____ 2. In the feeding area, the floor surface should be _____.

     A. washable           B. carpeted

Reason: _____

_____

_____ 3. To prevent back strain for adults, _____-high changing surfaces should be used.

     A. hip           B. waist

Reason: _____

_____

_____ 4. The sleeping area should be adjacent to the _____ area.

     A. feeding           B. diapering

Reason: _____

_____

_____ 5. To create a separate play area for babies who crawl, _____ dividers should be used.

     A. low           B. high

Reason: _____

_____

_____ 6. In crowded areas toddlers are inclined to _____.

     A. cry           B. withdraw

Reason: _____

_____

_____ 7. A carpeted floor in the play area will be _____ for crawling children.

     A. warmer           B. uncomfortable

Reason: _____

_____

*(Continued)*

_____ 8. The sleeping area usually uses the _____ space.

     A. least              B. most

Reason: _____

_____

_____ 9. Infants _____ need a darkened room to sleep.

     A. do                B. do not

Reason: _____

_____

_____ 10. With infants and toddlers, routines are _____ time-consuming than with other preschool children.

     A. more             B. less

Reason: _____

_____

_____ 11. Toddlers need more _____ spaces than infants do.

     A. closed           B. open

Reason: _____

_____

_____ 12. The _____ area for toddlers should be located near the main entrance.

     A. receiving        B. diapering

Reason: _____

_____

_____ 13. Toddlers need one-third to _____ of the total classroom space open for play.

     A. one-half         B. three-fourths

Reason: _____

_____

_____ 14. Teachers of infants and toddlers usually prefer _____ flooring.

     A. tile              B. carpeted

Reason: _____

_____

_____ 15. The outdoor play areas should have a large, _____ area.

     A. paved           B. grassy

Reason: _____

_____

# Toys for Development

Name _____

Date _____ Period_____

Clip pictures of toys from magazines or toy catalogs that promote fine motor, gross motor, reaching and grasping, and sound activities. Mount the pictures in the appropriate spaces. If pictures are unavailable, sketch the toys.

| Fine Motor | Gross Motor |
|---|---|
|  |  |
| **Reaching and Grasping** | **Sounds** |
|  |  |

# Child Care Procedures

Name _____

Date _____ Period_____

The following story tells about Jan's first morning as an assistant in a child care center. Jan makes several mistakes. Read the story and find her errors. In the space provided, explain Jan's errors and tell what she should do in the future to avoid repeating the errors.

## A New Job for Jan

Monday was Jan's first day assisting at the local child care center. She was thrilled to have gotten the job, and she began the day with enthusiasm.

Jan's first task was to greet parents and their children as they arrived in the receiving area. Five-month-old Timmy Henson began to cry as soon as Jan took him from his father. She quickly ran and placed him in a crib so she could greet other children. Surely Timmy would stop crying soon. Jan continued the morning by first reading a story to several children and then helping to supervise a painting activity.

Time was passing quickly, and Jan realized it was time for a diaper check. The infants were all awake except for Maria and Tom. Jan gently woke them. Tom did not need a change, but Maria was wet. Jan placed Maria on the floor and knelt down next to the crib to change her. Maria was crying, so Jan gave her a pacifier that she found on the floor. Maria was soon content.

As Jan was putting the clean diaper on Maria, she was called to help prepare the morning snack. Jan threw the dirty diaper in the garbage and wiped her hands on her pants. She picked up Maria and returned her to the crib to finish her nap.

Jan then went directly to the kitchen area where she began to cut up apples and cheese for the children's snack. She took the snack to the toddlers who were playing in the gross motor area. Jan was very tired after her busy morning, so she decided to take a break and read a magazine.

What mistakes did Jan make during her first morning on the job? What can she do to avoid making these mistakes in the future? _____

_____

_____

_____

_____

_____

_____

_____

_____

_____

_____

_____

_____

_____

_____

_____

# Programs for School-Age Children  29

## Quality School-Age Programs

Activity A

Chapter 29

Name _____

Date _____ Period_____

Read the following statements. Circle *Y* if the statement is characteristic of a quality school-age program. Circle *N* if it is not.

Y  N   1.  Tailored to the needs, abilities, and interests of the children served.

Y  N   2.  Mixed-age grouping is used to promote positive peer modeling and the development of leadership skills.

Y  N   3.  Teachers use time out to discipline children.

Y  N   4.  Schedules are rigid to teach children self-discipline.

Y  N   5.  Children are allowed to help plan curriculum and make choices about activities.

Y  N   6.  Environments are entirely designed to promote large group activities.

Y  N   7.  Activities are designed to encourage the children to think, reason, question, and experiment.

Y  N   8.  Activities foster a sense of dependence.

Y  N   9.  Most adult-child interaction takes the form of instruction and verbal directions.

Y  N  10.  Staff seek meaningful conversations with children.

Y  N  11.  Staff recognize a child's efforts as well as accomplishments.

Y  N  12.  A child's treatment by staff depends on the child's cultural background.

Y  N  13.  Staff work with children to set clear limits.

Y  N  14.  Motor activities focus on competitive games.

Y  N  15.  A variety of materials is available for arts and crafts.

Y  N  16.  Activities are designed to advance development.

Y  N  17.  The reason for limits and expectations are explained to children.

Y  N  18.  Staff include the children in problem-solving situations.

Y  N  19.  Outdoor activities are limited to competitive games.

Y  N  20.  Staff work in partnership with parents to meet each child's goals.

# My Ideal Environment

Name _____

Date _____ Period_____

Pretend you are 10 years old. Your parents have arranged for you to attend an after-school program until they can pick you up at 5:30 each weekday evening. Describe your ideal environment for the center where you will be. Include both indoor (interest center, quiet areas, open areas) and outdoor space. Describe each area thoroughly, including floor coverings, wall coverings, furniture, and equipment. Keep in mind that this environment must meet the requirements of a quality school-age program.

| Indoor Space |
|---|
| General description of my ideal indoor space: |
| Interest centers in my ideal center: |
| Quiet areas in my ideal center: |
| Open areas in my ideal center: |

| Outdoor Space |
|---|
| General description of my ideal outdoor space: |

# Design a Survey

Name _____

Date _____ Period_____

Design a survey to be used with school-age children to assess their interests. This information would be used to plan the curriculum for an after-school program. Begin by choosing a title for your survey. Then include the questions or incomplete sentences that you would use in the survey.

Title: _____

_____
_____
_____
_____
_____
_____
_____
_____
_____
_____
_____
_____
_____
_____
_____
_____
_____
_____
_____
_____
_____
_____
_____
_____
_____
_____
_____
_____
_____
_____
_____
_____

# Games for Fostering Development

Name _____

Date _____ Period_____

In a small group, brainstorm a list of games that school-age children would enjoy and that would also foster development: physical, cognitive, emotional, or social. List the games under one of the four categories shown below: board, card, indoor, or outdoor games. Then indicate the type of development each would foster.

| Board Games | |
|---|---|
| Name | Type of Development |
| | |
| | |
| | |
| | |
| | |
| | |
| | |
| | |
| | |
| | |
| | |
| | |

| Outdoor Games | |
|---|---|
| Name | Type of Development |
| | |
| | |
| | |
| | |
| | |
| | |
| | |
| | |
| | |
| | |
| | |
| | |

| Card Games | |
|---|---|
| Name | Type of Development |
| | |
| | |
| | |
| | |
| | |
| | |
| | |
| | |
| | |
| | |
| | |
| | |

| Indoor Games | |
|---|---|
| Name | Type of Development |
| | |
| | |
| | |
| | |
| | |
| | |
| | |
| | |
| | |
| | |
| | |
| | |

9. What is glaucoma? _____

_____

_____

_____

_____

10. How is glaucoma treated? _____

_____

_____

_____

11. What is the difference between nearsightedness and farsightedness? _____

_____

_____

_____

_____

12. Explain color deficiency. _____

_____

_____

_____

13. List at least three ways a teacher can help children who have visual disabilities. _____

_____

_____

_____

# Physical and Health Disorders

Name _____

Date _____ Period _____

Explain each of the following disorders and describe problems that a child with each disorder would face.

| Allergies | |
|---|---|
| Amputation | |
| Arthritis | |
| Asthma | |
| Cerebral palsy | |
| Cystic fibrosis | |
| Diabetes | |
| Epilepsy | |
| Hemophilia | |
| Leukemia | |
| Spina bifida | |

# Helping Children Who Have Special Needs

**Activity D**

**Chapter 30**

Name _____

Date _____ Period_____

Read a magazine or newspaper article that relates to teaching children with special needs in an inclusionary class-room. Write a report in the space provided. Then summarize what you feel are the most important considerations for teachers and what you learned from the article. Share this information orally with the class.

Title of article: _____

Source of article: _____

Report: _____

Summary comments (important considerations for teachers of children with special needs and what you learned from reading the article): _____

_____

_____

_____

_____

_____

_____

_____

_____

_____

_____

_____

_____

_____

_____

_____

_____

_____

_____

_____

_____

_____

_____

_____

_____

# The Child Who Is Gifted

Name _____

Date _____ Period_____

Interview a parent or teacher of a young child who has been identified as gifted to learn more about how to handle this special need. Ask the following questions.

What is the child's age? _____

In what area(s) is the child gifted? _____

_____

_____

How was the child identified as gifted? _____

_____

_____

What characteristics identify the child as being gifted? _____

_____

_____

_____

_____

What special programs have been made available at home, at school, and in the community to help meet the needs of the child who is gifted?_____

_____

_____

_____

Use the space below for more specific questions and answers related to the child you are studying.

_____

_____

_____

_____

_____

_____

_____

_____

_____

_____

_____

# Parent Involvement 31

## Getting Parents Involved

**Activity A**

**Chapter 31**

Name _____

Date _____ Period_____

Complete each of the following sentences using the correct word or words.

active
daily news flash
debating
e-mail
letters

newsletters
orientation
parent involvement
planning
positive

problem-solving file
professional
sunshine call
theme
traveling backpack

_____ 1. A telephone call made by a teacher to a parent to communicate praise and support for the child is referred to as a _____.

_____ 2. Many teachers use _____ to create parent newsletters.

_____ 3. _____ refers to patterns of participation in educational programs by parents.

_____ 4. To have a successful parent-teacher conference, you must first spend time _____.

_____ 5. Teachers can send children's favorite items home with one child at a time using a _____.

_____ 6. A letter or newsletter should be written using the _____ voice.

_____ 7. Information on problems parents may face can be organized into a _____.

_____ 8. Teachers get the most from parent volunteers when they provide a(n) _____ session.

_____ 9. The _____ is a written communication for parents that contains news about events and occasions at the center.

_____ 10. Letters sent to parents often include the _____ of the week.

_____ 11. _____ are written communications that often address only one subject and are put out on an "as needed" basis.

_____ 12. It is best to begin and end the parent-teacher conference with a _____ comment.

_____ 13. A problem that often occurs in group discussions is that groups begin _____ among themselves.

_____ 14. When meeting with parents, the teacher should always model _____ behavior.

_____ 15. _____ are written communications that include information concerning a variety of topics and are put out on a regular basis.

# Parent Letters

Name _____

Date _____ Period_____

Assume you are a teacher and have been asked to write the first letter of the year to parents. Write a letter in the active voice that includes the following information:

- An introduction of yourself and the other teachers.

- Classroom goals, limits, and expectations.

- An invitation to parents to observe and/or take part in the classroom.

_____

_____

_____

_____

_____

_____

_____

_____

_____

_____

_____

_____

_____

_____

_____

_____

_____

_____

_____

_____

_____

_____

_____

_____

_____

_____

_____

# Parent Discussion Groups

Name _____

Date _____ Period_____

In the chart below, list advantages and disadvantages of using discussion groups for teaching parenting information. Then use the chart to answer the questions that follow. Discuss your answers in class.

| Advantages of Discussion Groups | Disadvantages of Discussion Groups |
|---|---|
|  |  |

1. What do you think is the strongest argument in favor of using parent discussion? _____

_____

_____

_____

_____

*(Continued)*

2. Why might some parents dislike discussion groups? _____
_____
_____
_____
_____
_____

3. What do you think is the strongest argument against using parent discussion groups? Why? _____
_____
_____
_____
_____
_____
_____

# Teacher Hotline

Name _____

Date _____ Period_____

Pretend you are an advice columnist who writes a "Teacher Hotline" column for an educational journal. Answer the following letters from teachers about their concerns in working with parents.

*Dear Teacher Hotline:*
*I have difficulty working with parents. For some reason, when I point out the family's weaknesses, the parents get defensive. What should I do?*
*Signed,*
*A Discouraged Teacher*

Dear Discouraged Teacher:

_____

_____

_____

_____

_____

_____

Sincerely,
T.H.

*Dear Teacher Hotline:*
*My director has asked me to publish a newsletter. I am afraid to confess that I do not know what to include in the newsletter. What should I do? Help!*
*Signed,*
*A Confused Teacher*

Dear Confused Teacher:

_____

_____

_____

_____

_____

_____

Sincerely,
T.H.

*Dear Teacher Hotline,*
*Whenever parents visit my classroom, I feel uncomfortable. My pulse increases and I feel nervous. How can I relax?*
*Signed,*
*An Uncomfortable Teacher*

Dear Uncomfortable Teacher:

_____

_____

_____

_____

_____

_____

Sincerely,
T.H.

*Dear Teacher Hotline,*
*Last Tuesday I began my job as a head teacher in a new center. My director has asked me to write the first parent letter. My concern is how to make parent letters interesting. Can you help?*
*Signed,*
*A Questioning Teacher*

Dear Questioning Teacher:

_____

_____

_____

_____

_____

_____

Sincerely,
T.H.

*(Continued)*

*Dear Teacher Hotline:*

How important are first impressions? Last week I had my first parent-teacher conference. Without thinking I told a parent that his child was a brat. The father got angry and walked out. Now what do I do?

Signed,
Out of Answers

Dear Out of Answers:

_____
_____
_____
_____
_____
_____
_____

Sincerely,
T.H.

*Dear Teacher Hotline:*

I am embarrassed that I don't know what to do! On Thursday I had a conference with a timid parent. This mother couldn't even hold eye contact with me. We scheduled a continuation of the conference next week. How can I make the mother feel more comfortable?

Signed,
Embarrassed

Dear Embarrassed:

_____
_____
_____
_____
_____
_____
_____

Sincerely,
T.H.

*Dear Teacher Hotline:*

The staff at my school are having a difficult time scheduling parent-teacher conferences. We are allowed to use the time from 4 to 5 p.m. for this activity three days a month. What should we do?

Signed,
No Answers

Dear No Answers:

_____
_____
_____
_____
_____
_____

Sincerely,
T.H.

*Dear Teacher Hotline:*

I am working with a parent who insists that I spank his child. How can I convince this father that spanking isn't successful?

Sincerely,
Opposed

Dear Opposed:

_____
_____
_____
_____
_____
_____

Sincerely,
T.H.

## Assessing Your Abilities

**Activity A**

**Chapter 32**

Name _____

Date _____ Period_____

Effective early childhood teachers have many abilities in common. To find out how your abilities compare, rate your skills in these areas by checking the appropriate blank for each item.

| Strongly Agree | Agree | Disagree | Strongly Disagree | |
|---|---|---|---|---|
| ____ | ____ | ____ | ____ | 1. Interacts well with children. |
| ____ | ____ | ____ | ____ | 2. Interacts well with adults. |
| ____ | ____ | ____ | ____ | 3. Demonstrates teamwork skills. |
| ____ | ____ | ____ | ____ | 4. Works well as a leader. |
| ____ | ____ | ____ | ____ | 5. Communicates well verbally. |
| ____ | ____ | ____ | ____ | 6. Communicates well in writing. |
| ____ | ____ | ____ | ____ | 7. Has solid computer skills. |
| ____ | ____ | ____ | ____ | 8. Listens effectively to others. |
| ____ | ____ | ____ | ____ | 9. Understands child development. |
| ____ | ____ | ____ | ____ | 10. Comforts, nurtures, and praises children effectively. |
| ____ | ____ | ____ | ____ | 11. Effectively meets children's physical care and supervision needs. |
| ____ | ____ | ____ | ____ | 12. Follows ethical standards. |
| ____ | ____ | ____ | ____ | 13. Plans developmentally appropriate curriculum and themes. |
| ____ | ____ | ____ | ____ | 14. Uses positive guidance techniques. |
| ____ | ____ | ____ | ____ | 15. Makes sound decisions. |
| ____ | ____ | ____ | ____ | 16. Solves problems well. |
| ____ | ____ | ____ | ____ | 17. Leads group activities effectively. |
| ____ | ____ | ____ | ____ | 18. Observes and assesses behavior objectively. |
| ____ | ____ | ____ | ____ | 19. Develops appropriate routines, transitions, and schedules. |
| ____ | ____ | ____ | ____ | 20. Plans or serves nutritious meals and snacks. |
| ____ | ____ | ____ | ____ | 21. Sets and enforces effective limits for children's behavior. |
| ____ | ____ | ____ | ____ | 22. Demonstrates first-aid techniques and emergency procedures. |
| ____ | ____ | ____ | ____ | 23. Plans effective activity areas. |
| ____ | ____ | ____ | ____ | 24. Selects safe and appropriate toys, software, and playground equipment. |

# Know How to Job Hunt

Name _____

Date _____ Period_____

Decide whether the following statements about job hunting are true or false. Circle *T* if the statement is true or *F* if the statement is false.

T   F   1.   Recent graduates should not list lab work or volunteer work in their field of study on a resume.

T   F   2.   The ideal time to ask about vacations is during your interview.

T   F   3.   In nearly all interviews, applicants are given the opportunity to ask questions.

T   F   4.   A brief thank-you note sent soon after an interview is a basic courtesy that serves as a reminder to those you met.

T   F   5.   Sending a thank-you note by e-mail is never appropriate.

T   F   6.   Keeping a mental record of each cover letter you send is sufficient.

T   F   7.   You should try to state success incidents and accomplishments in your interview.

T   F   8.   Asking questions of your supervisor and fellow employees will help you learn more about your job and improve your skills.

T   F   9.   Interviewers cannot legally ask certain questions because they may be discriminatory.

T   F   10.   A resume is a brief summary of your qualifications, skills, and job experiences.

T   F   11.   Networking means developing a group of professional contacts.

T   F   12.   The hidden job market involves jobs that are advertised informally through word of mouth.

T   F   13.   When employers evaluate a resume, they look for gaps in employment dates, the amount of space given to earlier jobs, and the emphasis on education.

T   F   14.   Newspapers list all job titles related to child care under "child care teacher."

T   F   15.   As long as you have sent a resume in advance, you do not need to take a resume to the interview.

T   F   16.   You should be careful not to volunteer negative information about former employers or yourself during an interview.

T   F   17.   When interviewers ask about your weaknesses, answer as quickly as possible and then change the subject.

T   F   18.   Reading newspaper ads once a week is more efficient than reading them every day.

T   F   19.   Being involved in professional organizations does little to help in the job search.

T   F   20.   Your resume may serve as your own self-inventory.

# A Job Application

Name _____

Date _____ Period _____

Complete the following job application form. When you are finished, divide into small groups and evaluate one another's applications.

## Community Child Care Center

**NAME AND ADDRESS**

| First Name | Middle Name | Last Name | Social Security No. | Date of Application |
|---|---|---|---|---|
|  |  |  |  |  |

| PERMANENT MAILING ADDRESS | | | | TELEPHONE NO. |
|---|---|---|---|---|
| Number and street | City | State | Zip code | (Area) Local Number |
|  |  |  |  |  |

| Are you over 18 years of age and less than 70? |
|---|

**JOB INTEREST**

| Title of position for which you are applying: |
|---|
| Full-Time ☐   Part-Time ☐   Permanent ☐   Temporary ☐   Summer ☐ |
| Are you currently employed?   Yes ☐   No ☐   Date available to start: |

**EDUCATION AND TRAINING**

| Name and Address (City & State) of last Grade School Attended | Dates Attended | Major Studies | Did You Graduate? Yes ☐ No ☐ |
|---|---|---|---|
|  |  |  |  |

| Name and Address (City & State) of last High School Attended | Dates Attended | Major Studies | Did You Graduate? Yes ☐ No ☐ |
|---|---|---|---|
|  |  |  |  |

| Name and Address (City & State) of Business Career or Technical School Attended | Dates Attended | Major Studies | Did You Graduate? Yes ☐ No ☐ |
|---|---|---|---|
|  |  |  |  |

| COLLEGE LEVEL AND ABOVE (Including Junior & Community Colleges) | | | | |
|---|---|---|---|---|
| SCHOOL NAME | SCHOOL LOCATION (City & State) | DATE GRADUATED (or Years attended) Month/Year | TYPE OF DEGREE RECEIVED | MAJOR & MINOR FIELD OF STUDY |
|  |  |  |  |  |
|  |  |  |  |  |
|  |  |  |  |  |

| Your College Grade Point Average = |
|---|
| A =                                          Lowest Passing = |
| Awards or Honors: |
| Special Skills: |
| Professional Memberships related to the position: |

*(Continued)*

## EMPLOYMENT RECORD

Please list every employer, including part-time. Begin with your present or most recent employer.

| Date | Name & Address— Employer | 1 Position or Occupation 2 Department 3 Name of supervisor | Describe Major Duties | Salary or Wages (Monthly) | Reason for leaving |
|---|---|---|---|---|---|
| From<br>Month/Year<br>To<br>Month/Year | | 1<br>2<br>3 | | Starting<br>$____<br>Final<br>$____ | |
| From<br>Month/Year<br>To<br>Month/Year | | 1<br>2<br>3 | | Starting<br>$____<br>Final<br>$____ | |
| From<br>Month/Year<br>To<br>Month/Year | | 1<br>2<br>3 | | Starting<br>$____<br>Final<br>$____ | |
| From<br>Month/Year<br>To<br>Month/Year | | 1<br>2<br>3 | | Starting<br>$____<br>Final<br>$____ | |

## REFERENCES (do not list relatives)

| Name | Address | Phone No. | Occupation | Years Known |
|---|---|---|---|---|
| | | | | |
| | | | | |
| | | | | |

## ADDITIONAL DATA

Have you ever been convicted of a crime  (other than traffic or other minor violations)     Yes ☐     No ☐
that would affect your job performance?
If yes, give nature of offence and other circumstances regarding conviction.

Are you a U.S. citizen?                                                                    Yes ☐     No ☐
If "No," do you have an alien registration card or valid U.S. work permit?   Yes ☐     No ☐

Non-English languages you read                          speak                          write

Other special skills, knowledges and abilities which support your qualifications for the position you are seeking:

## PHYSICAL STATUS

Do you have any disabilities that would affect your job performance?     Yes ☐     No ☐
If yes, explain:

In completing, and submitting this application, I understand and agree: That any misstatement of material facts will be sufficient reason for immediate withdrawal of this application or, in the event of employment be deemed cause for dismissal. That my previous employers may be asked for information concerning my employment, character, ability, and experiences. That no question on this application has been answered in such a manner as to disclose my race, religion, or national origin. That if employed, I may be required to furnish proof of age by birth or baptismal certificate.

Signature _____     Date of Application _____

# Balancing Multiple Roles

**Activity D**

**Chapter 32**

Name _____

Date _____ Period_____

Interview an early childhood professional using the questions listed below. Ask this person how he or she balances multiple roles. Record the person's responses in the space provided.

Professional's Name and Position: _____

1. Please list all the roles you have, including family, work, and community roles. _____
   _____
   _____
   _____

2. Which of your roles is the most demanding on your time? the least? Explain. _____
   _____
   _____
   _____
   _____

3. Do you ever feel stressed trying to meet the demands of all your roles? Explain. _____
   _____
   _____
   _____
   _____
   _____

4. Which roles do you find conflict the most? Explain. _____
   _____
   _____
   _____
   _____

5. When two roles compete for the same time, how do you decide which one takes priority? _____
   _____
   _____
   _____
   _____

*(Continued)*

6.  What time-management strategies do you use to help you reduce role strain? _____

    _____

    _____

    _____

    _____

    _____

7.  What three tips would you offer a new professional for balancing multiple roles? _____

    _____

    _____

    _____

    _____

    _____

# Lesson Plan Form

**Name** _____

**Date** _____ **Period** _____

Group: _____

Name of Activity: _____

Date scheduled: _____ Time scheduled: _____

Developmental goals: _____

_____

_____

_____

_____

_____

_____

_____

Learning objective: _____

_____

_____

_____

_____

_____

Materials needed: _____

_____

_____

_____

_____

_____

Motivation/introduction: _____

_____

_____

_____

_____

_____

_____

*(Continued)*

Procedures: _____

_____

_____

_____

_____

_____

_____

Closure/transition: _____

_____

_____

_____

Evaluation:

A. The Activity: Selection and Development _____

_____

_____

_____

_____

_____

_____

B. The Children's Responses _____

_____

_____

_____

_____

_____

_____

C. Teaching Strategies _____

_____

_____

_____

_____

_____

_____

# Lesson Plan Form

**Name** _____

**Date** _____ **Period** _____

Group: _____

Name of Activity: _____

Date scheduled: _____Time scheduled: _____

Developmental goals: _____

_____

_____

_____

_____

_____

_____

_____

Learning objective: _____

_____

_____

_____

_____

_____

Materials needed: _____

_____

_____

_____

_____

_____

Motivation/introduction: _____

_____

_____

_____

_____

_____

_____

*(Continued)*

Procedures: _____

_____

_____

_____

_____

_____

_____

_____

Closure/transition: _____

_____

_____

_____

Evaluation:

A. The Activity: Selection and Development _____

_____

_____

_____

_____

_____

B. The Children's Responses _____

_____

_____

_____

_____

_____

C. Teaching Strategies _____

_____

_____

_____

_____

_____

_____

# Lesson Plan Form

Name _____

Date _____ Period _____

Group: _____

Name of Activity: _____

Date scheduled: _____ Time scheduled: _____

Developmental goals: _____

_____

_____

_____

_____

_____

_____

Learning objective: _____

_____

_____

_____

_____

Materials needed: _____

_____

_____

_____

_____

Motivation/introduction: _____

_____

_____

_____

_____

_____

*(Continued)*

Procedures: _____

_____

_____

_____

_____

_____

_____

Closure/transition: _____

_____

_____

_____

Evaluation:

A. The Activity: Selection and Development _____

_____

_____

_____

_____

_____

B. The Children's Responses _____

_____

_____

_____

_____

C. Teaching Strategies _____

_____

_____

_____

_____

_____

# Lesson Plan Form

**Name** _____

**Date** _____ **Period** _____

Group: _____

Name of Activity: _____

Date scheduled: _____ Time scheduled: _____

Developmental goals: _____

_____

_____

_____

_____

_____

_____

_____

Learning objective: _____

_____

_____

_____

_____

_____

Materials needed: _____

_____

_____

_____

_____

_____

Motivation/introduction: _____

_____

_____

_____

_____

_____

_____

_____

*(Continued)*

**Name** _____

Procedures: _____

_____

_____

_____

_____

_____

_____

Closure/transition: _____

_____

_____

_____

Evaluation:

A. The Activity: Selection and Development _____

_____

_____

_____

_____

B. The Children's Responses _____

_____

_____

_____

_____

C. Teaching Strategies _____

_____

_____

_____

_____

_____

# Lesson Plan Form

Name _____

Date _____ Period _____

Group: _____

Name of Activity: _____

Date scheduled: _____ Time scheduled: _____

Developmental goals: _____

_____

_____

_____

_____

_____

_____

_____

Learning objective: _____

_____

_____

_____

_____

_____

Materials needed: _____

_____

_____

_____

_____

_____

Motivation/introduction: _____

_____

_____

_____

_____

_____

_____

_____

*(Continued)*

Name _____

Procedures: _____

_____

_____

_____

_____

_____

_____

_____

Closure/transition: _____

_____

_____

_____

_____Evaluation:

A. The Activity: Selection and Development _____

_____

_____

_____

_____

_____

_____

B. The Children's Responses _____

_____

_____

_____

_____

_____

_____

C. Teaching Strategies _____

_____

_____

_____

_____

_____

_____